He didn't star

He didn't start out as an executive, an executive assistant or even as a male secretary. Brantley was sent to the place fabled in song and story, the place that has come to represent the dregs, the dumps, the bog from which workers either ascend or are sucked under for good.

The mailroom.

MICHAEL J. FOX

IN

THE SECRET OF MY SUCCESS

■ A **RASTAR** PRODUCTION A **HERBERT ROSS** FILM ■
■ MICHAEL J. FOX ■
■ "THE SECRET OF MY SUCCESS" ■
■ HELEN SLATER ■
■ RICHARD JORDAN ■ MARGARET WHITTON ■
■ SCREENPLAY BY **JIM CASH** & **JACK EPPS, JR.** ■
■ AND **AJ CAROTHERS** ■
■ STORY BY **AJ CAROTHERS** ■
■ EXECUTIVE PRODUCER **DAVID CHASMAN** ■
■ PRODUCED AND DIRECTED BY **HERBERT ROSS** ■

FROM
RASTAR

A **UNIVERSAL** Picture
© 1986 by Universal City Studios Inc.

THE SECRET
OF MY SUCCESS

Martin Owens

**Based on a screenplay by
Jim Cash & Jack Epps, Jr.
and AJ Carothers**

CORGI BOOKS

THE SECRET OF MY SUCCESS

A CORGI BOOK   0 552 13276 4

First publication in Great Britain

PRINTING HISTORY
Corgi edition published 1987

This book is set in 10/11pt Times

Corgi Books are published by Transworld Publishers Ltd.,
61–63 Uxbridge Road, Ealing, London W5 5SA,
in Australia by Transworld Publishers (Aust.) Pty. Ltd.,
15–23 Helles Avenue, Moorebank, NSW 2170, and in New
Zealand by Transworld Publishers (N.Z.) Ltd., Cnr. Moselle
and Waipareira Avenues, Henderson, Auckland.

Printed and bound in Great Britain by
Hazell Watson & Viney Limited,
Member of the BPCC Group,
Aylesbury, Bucks

THE SECRET
OF MY SUCCESS

CHAPTER ONE

Somewhere in this city, Brantley Foster thought, there is
an office with my name on it.

He had this confident expectation as his bus careened
onto Eighth Avenue. It headed towards the Port Auth-
ority Terminal on Forty-Second Street in the heart of
New York City. As he looked through his curved and
tinted window, the Young Kansan saw a whole city busy
doing business.

The first businessman he saw was an enterprising pimp
standing near a group of his colleagues on the corner. He
wore the pimp's equivalent of a three-piece suit: a suede
jacket with fur at the collar, brown leather pants and a
safari hat with a feather dancing at the top. Brantley
approved of his 'Dress for Success' wardrobe and the 'go
for it' spirit of his stance.

As the bus pulled into the darkness of the terminal, he
saw another representative of the New York business-
world. A prostitute stood against a newsstand, throwing
suggestive but purposely vague suggestions ('Want a
date?' 'Want to go out?') at male passersby. Brantley was
also impressed by *her* workclothes — a black-and-white
miniskirt, net stockings and a halter top — and by *her*
confident, no-nonsense attitude. She was a comer, all
right, he thought. Then with a grin, he privately
corrected himself. She was a mover and a shaker. He
smiled again and shook his head. She was a girl on the go.

They were *all* on the go, all the people of New York,
that's what Brantley thought — whether they were

moving up in an office building or just up the stairs of a cheap hotel to a bedroom. All of New York was in a hurry. And I'm one of them now, Brantley thought. The bus came to a sudden, definitive halt.

'Well, Toto,' Brantley said to himself, 'I guess we're not in Kansas any more.'

He had wanted New York; no other place would do. Other cities had their success stories: Chicago had its successful gangsters; Houston had its booming gun salesmen; Boston had people who excelled at inheriting wealth. But only New York had all of those things and more. And now only New York had Brantley Foster.

His parents, of course, had wanted any place but New York. Kansas was their first choice; Kansas was also their last choice. It had been strange enough for them to see their son attend and succeed in college. For Brantley at 23 to then declare he was leaving town — leaving the state, in fact — was almost more than they could take.

'New York City,' his father had just kept repeating, as if it were a disease with which he would have to accept being stricken. 'New York City.'

His mother, as always, was more open.

'He wants to see what's there,' she had said. Her tone suggested Brantley would peek in, pay his respects, and then come right back home.

'I can tell him what's there,' his father replied, his voice dripping with Sex, Drugs, Corruption and Death.

'I don't know how,' his mother said, reasonably, 'when you've never been there.'

It had always been this way: the large, burly father coping decently but inarticulately; the small, birdlike mother explaining innocently but understandingly. And in the center of them their slight, pleasant-faced, fair-haired boy, who had aspirations that needed to be explained and understood.

As he was handed his bag from the belly of the bus, Brantley thought he couldn't blame them. Why *wouldn't*

8

he want to run a general store or sell feed or drive a car for the druggist? It had been good enough for the children of their friends.

Brantley Foster, however, the young man himself thought, was different.

'I'm still against this,' his father had said.

'It's something I have to do,' Brantley had answered, as if his ambition had stolen his will, he couldn't help it.

'Well, I just can't figure out why you'd want to go off to New York when we've got everything here.'

His father pointed at the sparse kitchen, consisting of a shabby table and two tattered chairs. Then, to further reinforce his case, he pointed out their window to a barren back lawn on which one moss-covered swing stood. Then his father brought up both his hands, as if to say, What more could you want from life?

His mother only sighed. 'Did you pack an iron like I told you to?'

Brantley had been annoyed at his mother's protectiveness, but at least she assumed he was going. His father had just stood there, shaking his head, amazed at how the young threw away the true riches of the world. He toyed with a broken wooden salt shaker, affectionately.

'Oh, Mom . . . ' Brantley said, impatiently.

'You're gonna walk around wrinkled in New York City without an iron.'

Brantley grinned now, as he emerged from the dark terminal and left its stench behind. You could get by wrinkled in New York. He did not think the pimp of the corner would shout, 'Yo, youngblood! Use an iron next time, okay?'

You could get by wrinkled but not slow, not insecure and not lazy. Everyone moving past him had a determined, ambitious, intrepid air, even if they just intended to mail a letter. Lugging his enormous case, Brantley tried to keep up with them.

With the young businessman, straightening his tie and

9

looking at his watch. With a beautiful, painfully thin young woman — who was a ballet dancer, it looked like. With the black man, checking the lock on his briefcase. With the Asian man carrying what seemed a samples case. With that strange Rabbi-type guy with lots of sideburns who was crossing against the light.

In Kansas, there hardly *were* any of these people. In New York, they all had places to be — immediately.

'There's a world out there, Mom,' he had said to her in private later. 'Big and exciting. I've got a nice, small apartment. I've lined up a great job and I want to make lots of money.'

His voice had lowered then, almost to a reverent tone. 'I want to have a meaningful experience with an incredibly desirable woman. I can't take a woman like that to a small apartment. I've got to have a penthouse. I'm really doing this as much for you as for me. I want to make all those years in college pay off.'

His mother had nodded, as if picking up what she could of a foreign tongue. He had touched her hand, thanking her for making any effort his way. He thought she would be proud of him now, standing as he was on a corner with two black men, a Spanish child and a woman with incredibly spiky hair.

He smiled at them. Only the child smiled back.

'Take this,' she had said. His mother had forced a small folded paper into his palm. 'It's Uncle Howard's phone number in New York.'

This was a treasure she had given him, Brantley knew. It was like one of those bank accounts you keep only for emergencies; his mother was opening it for him. He stared at the crudely written digits as if they stood for a phenomenal amount of money and not a phone number.

He passed a store selling fancy hanging plants and cacti, young black women wearing beads in their corn rows, dogs riding in limousines. He felt the number in his inside coat pocket; it was his failsafe, it was his insurance.

10

He would use it if all else failed. And all else wouldn't fail.

As he smiled at the workman rolling a rack of furs or checked out the girls sunbathing on a roof, he felt he was already — though only minutes in Manhattan — on his way up.

Then he saw his apartment house.

Brantley checked the address in his pocket again. Three hundred and twenty-five West Forty-Sixth street. That was what the piece of paper said; that was what the door of the building said.

He felt a little dazed. He understood he would be roughing it; everyone in New York did at first. But wasn't this a tad *too* rough?

It was a small, squat, run-down tenement. The fire escape sagged, miserably, as if ready to faint into the street. The windows were all without exception shielded by large, sturdy, oppressive-looking gates. The facade had not been painted for what seemed decades.

Brantley sighed. Then he shrugged to himself. How would he have any basis for comparison if he did not start out in a place like this? Who would say they knew him 'when' if there was never any 'when' in which to be known? He thought harder but could come up with no more rationalizations. So he trudged up the cracked steps to the front door. It was, of course, unlocked.

The Super who greeted Brantley looked like a human offspring of the house itself. His two hundred-odd pounds had been crammed into a five foot three body; his very face seemed crushed, the cheeks pushed out, the eyes bulged. At fifty, he was half as old as the house; but he, too, cried out silently for gentrification.

'Follow me,' he said.

To Brantley's surprise — and dismay — they walked down instead of up. Down a twisting, creaking stairway to a boiler room and basement. The black of its interior was interrupted nowhere by sunlight; the smell was pure,

11

uncut mildew.

'Follow me,' he said again.

They walked down a dirty hallway until, in the distance, Brantley could faintly make out a door. It seemed to lead to a room that, in unfree societies, would be used for interrogations. No one could hear you scream.

'The guy who lived in the apartment croaked,' the Super informed him. 'He lived here fifteen years and never gave me a problem.'

'Fifteen years,' Brantley said, quietly, 'without parole.'

Obliviously, the Super stopped at the door. He took out a jangling ring which held a mass of cell keys.

'Died right in this apartment,' he said. 'Dead three days. What a stink.'

He found the right key. Then with some effort, he forced it into the rusted keyhole. He fumbled with it for what seemed an eternity, cursing quietly to himself. Finally, with a great effort, he managed to turn the key. Then using his meaty shoulder, he pushed the door slowly open.

The apartment no longer smelled like a corpse; this was a plus to Brantley's mind. It did, however, seem like a suitable home for one no longer living. It was a tiny 'studio,' which had already and for years been furnished. That meant it contained a rickety bed that — with two tattered bolsters — doubled as a couch; a flimsy table standing precariously on spindly legs; two old wooden chairs and a lamp. There was one window that looked out on a wall. An indecipherable graffiti message had been written there, as if in greeting to Brantley.

There was no training for actors in Kansas. Brantley's face plainly showed the way he was feeling.

'What did you expect,' the Super said, 'the Waldorf?'

Then the same combination of making excuses and making do came over Brantley. Wouldn't his penthouse look so much better after this? Might not a woman feel

12

pity for him — and even love — upon arriving? Most importantly of all, did he have any choice?

'No complaints,' Brantley said.

The Super nodded, as if glad to hear it. Then he immediately turned around and without a welcome, a warning or indeed another word, left the room.

Brantley stood there a minute. He looked around at the place, which was as big as one of his parents' storage closets at home. The size of the room suddenly made sense to him. New York was teeming with people, and more people teemed in every day. Everyone was there looking for a big break, a perfect mate, and a place to live. Brantley was now one of them.

That meant, of course, he was a speck, a dot, a pinpoint in a great metropolis. But unlike so many others, he had a job: his work address tickled at him in his pants pocket. He also had what few others in the entire world had: blind, ignorant, foolish, fortunate faith.

What he lacked in experience, in wisdom, in savvy — even in height, at only five foot five — he compensated for in confidence.

He started by confidently addressing his first companions.

'If there are any bugs in here or rats,' he announced, 'or anything else that has more legs than I do, you stay in your part of the room and I'll stay in mine.' He glanced at his luggage. 'I should warn you, I'm packing an iron.'

It was with his iron — his mother's iron — that he spent much of his first evening. With an old plank as an ironing board, he used it to press his only blue suit. The suit in which he would go to work tomorrow.

Yes, Brantley Foster thought, somewhere in this city, there is an office with my name on it.

He could not have known, of course, that the name on his office would be someone else's.

13

CHAPTER TWO

The next morning, Brantley Foster confidently boarded the New York city subway. He easily rode the Double-R train to Times Square, then without a hitch found the shuttle to Grand Central Station. He emerged unscathed, undaunted, hardly even sweating. A man must apply himself to mass transit as he applies himself to his career, he thought.

Brantley looked around for corroberation from his new 'fellow' New Yorkers: most were too dazed by their ordeal on the trains to reply. Oblivious to their agony, he strode across East Forty-Second Street until he hit the wide, inviting area of Third Avenue, home of his new job.

It had all been remarkably easy, he thought. He just mailed in his résumé, a thoughtful 'essay' on why he wanted the job, and numerous recommendations from his favorite professors. The reply had been swift and enthusiastic: Arnold Forbush of KRS, Inc wanted to hire Brantley Foster.

When Brantley stood at last outside the enormous headquarters, he felt suddenly less small. He felt that by being accepted by this company, he was growing slowly in stature: from speck to morsel, from amoeba to crumb. Straightening the tie on his — fully pressed — blue suit, he entered the building.

He scanned carefully the huge lobby directory, Farraway, Filbert, Forlorn — Forbush. As soon as his eye hit the name, however, the letters suddenly began to dance. Brantley began to doubt his vision, until he turned to his left.

A man with a KRS insignia was removing it.

The man very calmly yanked out the Forbush name — with the cold precision one uses to peel a band-aid or yank a tooth. Then he dropped Forbush into his right jacket pocket, closed the pocket over him with finality, and walked away.

Brantley smiled a little, with confusion. Then he swiveled around for a better view of the lobby and — unfortunately — grew less bewildered.

A staff of furniture movers, all with KRS emblazoned on their bosoms, were carrying out an array of desks, chairs, and cabinets. Plants were piled high on dollies; paper boxes were full of pen sets, desk ornaments, clock radios.

Brantley moved over to get some information.

'I'm looking for Mr Forbush,' he said to one workman. 'Arnold Forbush?'

'Better hurry,' the man said.

The furniture was wheeled and pushed across the lobby into an elevator — and into someone else's office, Brantley assumed. The mocking laughter of the workmen faded as did the sounds of their labors.

Brantley re-checked the directory. Next to the gaping hole that once was Forbush stood the words Eighth Floor. Brantley managed to see them before corporate fingers removed and pocketed them, as well.

On the eighth floor, the action in the lobby was duplicated and magnified. The whole place seemed alive with change: all forms of furniture were being moved from one office to another. Employees carried personal belongings, panting, to elevators.

Perhaps this was some sort of monthly drill that KRS used to test worker stamina, Brantley thought. He swallowed, uncomfortably, not buying it himself.

With trepidation but terrible politeness, he

approached a young, frazzled female receptionist.

'Excuse me?' he said. 'Mr Forbush?'

The woman turned, offended, as if he believed her to be the man. Then she sighed, understanding, and her expression turned mournful instead.

'Two doors up on your right,' she said.

Brantley smiled with polite thanks. But all the way up the hall to Forbush's office, he had a terrible feeling of dread.

It was justified.

Arnold Forbush, the man who had hired Brantley, the man who would have been his first — and best, and most beloved — boss, was cleaning out his desk.

Forbush was a slight, agitated man who seemed bent from the severity of his woes. Sweat covered his face as he dumped out desk drawers into boxes. His glasses had slid down his soggy nose.

Brantley, however, saw no reason to jump to conclusions — not before they were shoved in his face, anyway. He put on his best, most ambitious, most confident voice.

'Mr Forbush?' he said, as he stood in the doorway. 'I'm Brantley Foster. From Kansas. You hired me. I start work here today.'

Each sentence seemed to be more of a cruel joke than the last to Forbush. He snuffed, snorted, sighed, smiled on hearing them.

'What's going on here, Mr Forbush?' Brantley asked.

Forbush looked up, holding a picture of his wife and children in his damp hand. 'You're fired, kid. Sorry.'

Brantley took this as he might a punch to the stomach. He felt himself move backwards a bit in the doorway; his knees almost gave way. Forbush only went back to his duties. He dumped his family into a box filled with office supplies.

'We all saw it coming,' he muttered. 'But we looked for some kind of miracle. The miracle never happened.'

'What *did* happen?' Brantley asked, his voice cracked.

17

'A hostile takeover.' Forbush spat out the words as if they meant a Russian invasion. 'Ninety percent of the people in the building are out on the street. You're one of the ninety percent. Tough break.'

Brantley turned several ways in the doorway, as if he were a hanged man helplessly twisting. Then he turned back to the only man he could trust, the only man he knew in New York.

'I was counting on this job,' he said. 'What do I do now?'

Forbush looked up again. He saw a boy standing in the — neatly ironed — suit of a man, his slight body contorting as if in desperate need to be relieved. Forbush was neither his friend nor his father and would never be his boss. He was now, in the pitiless job market that was New York, Brantley's competition.

'Punt,' he replied.

To be fired without being hired was not Brantley's idea of a good morning. He stood outside the KRS building, his tie askew, the first faint wrinkles appearing in the pants of his suit.

What kind of a city *was* this? A boy comes all the way from Kansas, takes an apartment in a section called — not ironically — 'Hell's Kitchen' and vows to work his way up, and this was the greeting he got? A big New York foot in his face? Brantley did not think he could have been any more crushed if the whole KRS building now fell on him.

'Okay, New York,' he said aloud. 'That's how you want it? Okay.'

Brantley felt his spine straightening, his jaw hardening, his bladder relaxing. He would not write on his résumé, 'May 6, 1986 — May 6, 1986' as his term of employment at KRS. Neither would he board another bus back to Kansas. He would walk until he found another job. He would find a place that wanted a man who would work from nine to five, not from nine to nine-

18

thirty. He would do what he had set out to do: succeed.

Brantley had succeeded at one thing already. As he walked up Third Avenue, he had become an official New Yorker. He now talked to himself and nobody noticed at all.

The first company Brantley approached also had three initials: TSS. Since he had never known what KRS stood for, he did not bother himself about this name, either.

The Personnel officer was a large, nondescript man by the name of Shaw. He had the bland, permanent, vaguely frightening smile of someone who had been indoctrinated and liked it and wanted even more indoctrination. He seemed to enjoy speaking for his company, with which he shared the intimacy of a lover.

He read Brantley's résumé carefully, politely, thoroughly. Then he seemed to re-read it, from bottom to top. Brantley feared he might read it upside down before he said anything. But finally he spoke.

'We need someone with experience,' he said.

Brantley sighed, deeply. He tried to retain his composure. 'But I can't get any experience until I get a job that gives me experience.'

Shaw nodded, kindly, having fully expected this reply. 'If we gave you a job just to give you experience, you would use that experience to get a better job and the experience would benefit someone else.'

Shaw was as protective of his company as a wife is of a husband. Brantley responded carefully but pointedly.

'But I was trained in college to handle a job like this. In a sense, I already have experience.'

This was extremely well-reasoned, Brantley thought. Even at school, they had called him 'The Junior Executive.' They had also called him 'The Sophomore Executive' and 'The Senior Executive.' Brantley thought such ridicule should pay off somehow.

'What you have is college experience,' Shaw said, simply, 'not the practical, hard-nosed business experience we're looking for. If you had joined our training program out of high school, you would be qualified for this job now.'

Brantley was stymied. 'Then why did I go to college?'

A million different, intriguing answers seemed to occur to Shaw. He chose the kindliest one.

'Had fun, didn't you?'

Brantley next slogged his way into the office of BSS, a company nearly indistinguishable from the last one. Brantley did not even inquire as to their product, let alone the meaning of their initials.

This time, however, he found himself sitting opposite someone much more pleasant. It was a plump and compassionate young woman named Miller. She read his résumé only once and with ever-growing interest.

'What impresses me most,' she said, upon finishing, 'is the amount of *experience* you picked up while attending college.'

Brantley beamed. He leaned back, confidently, in his chair. This was the place. 'I knew a college degree was worthless without practical, hard-nosed business experience.'

Miller could not get over it. She read aloud all of the impressive titles Brantley had amassed over his four-year stint. 'Assistant Personnel Manager, Jayhawk Communications . . . Junior Purchasing Agent, Midland Furniture . . . Vice President in Charge of Production, Central Manufacturing . . . ' She looked up at him. 'Outstanding.'

This was too good to be true. And that was the problem. Brantley leaned in, suddenly leery.

'You're not going to tell me I had too much experience, are you?'

'Certainly not,' Miller said. 'You're absolutely perfect for the job.'

Brantley could not contain himself. He saw his ratty little flat transformed into a two-bedroom penthouse. Marble bathtub, grand piano, a queen-sized bed for 'guests.' Even a microwave; he had promised his mother.

'All *right*!' he shouted.

Miller seemed to grow a little pale at his demonstration of pleasure. She cleared her throat, pensively.

'Except . . . '

But Brantley was on a roll. His own personal Jacuzzi, all kinds of tape and video equipment, even a specially broken table for when his Dad came to visit: he saw it all.

'No exception — please! I want this job. I *need* it. I can do it. Every place I've been today, there's always been something wrong. Too young, too old, too short, too tall. Whatever the exception is, I'll fix it. I can be older, I can be taller. I can be *anything*.'

Miller responded then, with real concern. 'Can you be a minority woman?'

The water stilled inside his Jacuzzi. His videotape machine turned off. An eviction notice appeared on his penthouse door. Brantley put his head in his hands and sighed.

What kind of city *was* this? It all had been going according to plan — a plan he had had in his head for years. Now suddenly, exposed to reality, it faded, like film exposed to the light.

He had one thing he had to do now, one desire that could not be denied him by New York, one thing any young executive wants after a day such as this one.

He wanted to call his mother.

Brantley did not even wait until he got home. At the nearest phone booth, he darted inside, like Clark Kent about to be made stronger. He did not even fish for change. He called Kansas collect.

As he heard the familiar, reassuring voice of his mother accept the charges, he saw something out of the corner of his eye. A young Cuban playing a Conga drum was being eyed suspiciously by two grungy-looking men. Brantley tried to ignore it as he responded to his mother's anxious queries.

'Doing great, Mom,' he said, with difficulty. 'This town is terrific. No, the people are really nice. The job?' Brantley felt a little faint as the fibs cascaded from his lips. 'Oh, I've got a fantastic office, a gorgeous secretary, the works. What?' He laughed. 'Of course, she can type.'

Old Mom, he thought; she's been watching too many TV shows. So have those two guys out in the street, moving like thugs, their hands conspicuously hidden in their pockets. Brantley breathed a little easier as they passed the Conga man, passed the telephone booth, and entered a liquor store.

'Come on,' he said, 'you shouldn't worry about me. What danger? New York is just like Kansas . . . intensified.'

He was about to spew more falsehoods when he heard a giant crash. Wheeling around in the booth, Brantley saw the window of the liquor store shatter and fall to pieces. He saw the musician grab his drum protectively and scramble away. Brantley instinctively lowered himself in the booth, until from the street he was only a bobbing cowlick talking on the telephone.

His knees flat on the filthy floor, he resumed the conversation with his Mom.

'That's just the TV. Sure. I've got a TV. I've got three of them.'

Sirens now blared from the 'TV' that was the strange reality of New York. The two men came running out of the store just as a police car skidded to a stop before them.

Brantley placed a finger into his ear to make out the soft midwestern sounds of his mother. 'What?'

Just then, bullets flew both ways above his head through the glass of the booth. Glass rained down on him; the booth shook from the impact.

'Uncle Howard?' he said. 'Oh, yeah, Uncle Howard. The phone number. Yeah, I've still got it here.'

Brantley's field of concentration was, understandably,

a little cluttered. He saw one of the robbers winged by a bullet. He saw his partner watch this action with horror, then quickly fling down his own gun. At the same time, he felt the phone number in his inside pocket heat up, as if it too were newly lodged in him.

He thought, this phone call could cost me more than any in my life. And *I'm* not even paying.

'No, I haven't had time to call Uncle Howard, but I'll probably bump into him . . . ' He saw the two cops rush forward to clamp the cuffs on their prey, ' . . . at the country club one of these days.'

He heard the cop car roar off with more sound of sirens. Then, brushing the bits of glass from his hair, he slowly made to stand.

'Hey, listen,' he said, 'I've got to go. Give Dad my love. I'll call you again, soon. Love you, too. Bye.'

Brantley slammed the phone down. Then he immediately pulled open the doors of the booth and took a great breath of the rancid air.

That night, Brantley stood looking vacantly out the one window of his room. In the alley outside, an old bag lady had settled for the night, leaning wearily against her belongings. At least, Brantley thought, I won't be alone again tonight.

He had fixed up the place a little — a plant here, a painting there — but no one would have mistaken it for a co-op. He toyed with the last of a TV dinner, which he had managed to only half-unfreeze. Then he emptied his pockets and stared again at the number.

It had meant to be for an emergency. His Uncle Howard's number was a last resort, a suicide pill. How had one day in New York ended up with his swallowing this?

'Take this,' his mother had said, when she placed it in his hand. 'It's Uncle Howard's phone number in New York.'

'I've got an uncle in New York?' Brantley had asked.

His mother had moved her head in a half-nod, half-shrug before replying. 'My cousin Ellen was married to his half-sister's nephew before she got bit by that dog and died.' Then her tone turned more confident. 'He's still kin and kin is kin.'

Brantley gripped the number tight in his fist now. Kin was kin. Some things were always true. Even in New York City.

CHAPTER THREE

His mother's cousin was married to Uncle Howard's nephew before Uncle Howard's half-sister died.

That wasn't it. His mother's cousin was married to Uncle Howard's half-sister before . . . Brantley still couldn't remember it before the subway stopped. He had had to transfer three times before he got on the right train; his confidence about everything was draining now. He only knew that East Fifty-Third Street was where he had to be: Citicorp Plaza.

He got out, the details of his family tree still floating confusedly through his mind. He walked until he found the huge, glass, sixty-storey building that said 'Pemrose Consolidated Industries.' He entered it, still muttering to himself.

When he reached the top floor, Brantley straightened his tie. He made his way to the executive suite with all the nervousness of a messenger bringing bad news. And the bad news was himself.

Even so, when he stood before his Uncle's secretary, he flashed an ingratiating smile. He was still Brantley Foster, after all, still the boy who would conquer New York. As soon as he got this one little formality out of the way: putting the bite on his rich Uncle.

Uncle Howard's secretary — her name plate read Maureen Scott — was a tailored, attractive, competent-looking woman of forty. She looked up at him, blankly. Ingratiating smile or no, he was the scum of the business world: a man without an appointment.

'I'd like to see Mr Prescott,' Brantley said.

'Do you have an appointment?'

Brantley barreled right through. 'I thought I'd surprise him.'

Maureen Scott's expression grew coldly comic. 'Mr Prescott doesn't like surprises.'

Brantley matched her. 'Everybody likes surprises.'

'Not Mr Prescott,' she said, the fun and games over, 'You can leave your name.'

'Brantley Foster.'

Somehow he hoped this name might mean something, might be included on a list of People To Always Let In. But it was not to be.

'Of?' Maureen Scott said.

'Kansas.'

Strained patience crept into Maureen Scott's voice. 'Of what company? What did you want to see Mr Prescott about?'

'About being his nephew.'

This stopped Maureen. She reappraised him, as if now she might not be able to be officious to him with impunity. 'Oh. Well. Why don't you have a seat. I'll see if I can work you into Mr Prescott's schedule.'

All through this exchange, Brantley had heard an unsettling sound coming from beyond Maureen Scott's desk. It was the muffled sound of a man's voice rising in an office. It wasn't rising with pleasure, either.

Brantley figured he had nothing to lose now; that is, he had everything and so nothing. When things became *so* serious, *so* do-or-die, there was an element of the absurd about them, he thought. He could always be a feed salesman back home.

With this attitude, he glanced over at a copying machine in the corner. Then he turned back to Maureen.

'May I use that?' he asked.

The secretary tried but could not see why not; she grudgingly nodded.

26

Brantley grinned. He walked over to the machine; he danced a bit around it, trying to feel it out. Then he decided just to go for it.

He pulled up the lid and pressed his face to the glass. Then he pressed the 'Print' button.

Green light flashed into his eyes; then white light traced him from hair to chin. He pulled back, satisfied, the impressions of his lips still pressed appealingly on the glass.

Within a minute, he had it: a negative image of his flattened face, the way it looked pressed for laughs against his Mom's car window.

Brantley turned the picture — a lovely likeness, he thought — over. Then he wrote on its back in big block letters: 'Brantley Foster — Multi-Talented Job Seeker and Nephew.'

He walked over calmly and handed the picture to Maureen Scott.

'Give Uncle Howard my card,' he said.

Maureen looked down at the peculiar image, then back up at her young visitor. 'Are you *really* Mr Prescott's nephew?'

Presumably Uncle Howard was not given to sucking face with a copier. 'In a roundabout sort of way.'

Even Maureen had to smile at this. Then her smile suddenly disappeared, no fault of Brantley's.

Uncle Howard's voice had risen enough to be audible. Much to Brantley's dismay, he could now make out his words loud and clear.

'You idiots!' he was screaming. 'You haven't got half a brain between you! I'm looking at a three hundred dollar deficit here because you idiots didn't anticipate the changing market!'

There was silence again. Brantley flinched openly then gave an awkward smile to Maureen.

'Uncle Howard?' he asked.

Her smile was more practiced. She nodded. There was

27

little chance for a conversation before it was time for flinching again.

'Now get out of here! All of you! Bring me back some new ideas that will work or I'll have your heads mounted on my wall!'

Each word was like someone flicking Brantley's face with a finger. He shook, shimmied and cringed.

Then Uncle Howard's door opened. Into the waiting room three men hurried, as if fleeing a fire. Brantley barely had time to acknowledge them before they scattered in different directions — one into an elevator, another down a stairwell, the last into a men's room. Then there was silence.

Maureen smiled sweetly at Brantley now, to show him a final kindness before his death. 'I'll see if I can get you in now.'

'Uh, thanks.'

Maureen picked up Brantley's Xeroxed face and took it with her into her boss' office. There was a pause before Brantley could make out the man's faint, bewildered replies.

'What? Who? Kansas?'

Sweat began to pour down Brantley's twitching face now. He looked like a man with a fever who was being electrocuted. Maybe the thing with the Xerox went a tad *too* far.

Before he could feel any more self-recrimination, Maureen had re-entered the waiting room. She seemed a bit shaken and a bit relieved, as she always did upon leaving Prescott's office.

'Mr Prescott will see you now,' she said.

Brantley nodded, accepting his fate — one he had begged for, after all. Taking a deep breath of courage, vowing to act like a man, he rose. He gave a last nod to Maureen Scott before leaving her sight. She nodded back, as if it had been nice to know him.

It took a minute before Brantley even saw his Uncle.

He was too busy being riveted to the man's view. Sixty storeys up, it showcased all of midtown Manhattan; it was a veritable landscape of power. Brantley felt watched now by *all* of the city's CEOs, not just one.

And this one was bad enough. Howard Prescott was a handsome, vital man in his late forties: trim, tanned, powerful. He was also at this moment — and at most other moments, it seemed — extremely angry. He sat behind a beautiful marble desk, swiveling in a plush leather chair. He held Brantley's 'card' in his hand. He looked up from it, very slowly.

'Clever,' he said.

Then his fingers closed over the paper like a wrecker over a tiny car. In a second, Brantley's face had been crushed and tossed easily across the room into the trash.

Brantley cleared his throat, watching his own image so swiftly become garbage. He swiveled uneasily in a chair opposite his Uncle.

'You're one of the Kansas Fosters,' Prescott said, dismissively. 'Shirttail relative, to say the least.'

'Look,' Brantley said, 'I know you've probably already told your secretary to get me out of here in five minutes.'

'Two.'

'Okay then, I'll get right to it. I need a job, Uncle Howard.'

The man across from him winced at the intimate form of address.

'Around here, I'm Mr Prescott.' He looked Brantley up and down, piteously. 'Do you even know what we *do* here?'

Brantley was ready. 'Yes, sir. Pemrose is a multi-national conglomerate with twenty-seven different divisions, with products ranging from dog food to missile guidance systems.'

Grudgingly, Prescott gave the boy some credit; he could not help but be impressed. Still, he intended to teach Brantley a few things.

'We have thirty thousand people,' he said, 'working in this building alone. Their accumulated salary is higher than the gross national product of half the nations in the Common Market. Last year, we borrowed more money from banks than Mexico did. All we need is our own flag and army and we'd be the fifteenth most powerful nation on Earth.'

Sitting there, Prescott indeed looked like some kind of general; more than that, he had the cold, unswerving self-assurance of a despot. And not a petty one, either.

Brantley was a bit frightened by him; but he felt the two of them were getting some kind of rapport now. He would not have been surprised if his Uncle complimented him on his 'spunk.' Just the way bosses did on TV.

'It's a great company, Uncle — Mr Prescott,' he said, eagerly. 'That's why I'm here.'

Prescott's left eyebrow rose at the idea that Brantley was 'offering' them his services. His voice grew softly ironic.

'What can you do for us, Brantley? What experience have you had?'

There was that word again. 'Experience' stuck into his confidence, like an arrow into a balloon. Brantley tried to trump up some answer, as he had so many times before. But now it wasn't in him. With so much at stake, with this his last resort — after today, he would be either financier or feed salesman — he decided to tell the truth.

'Practically none,' he said.

Before this, such an admission would have sapped Brantley's energy, sent him right down to the dumps. Today, though, he felt his fervor rising as he admitted to being more and more unqualified, rising finally to a crescendo of inexperience.

'But I believe in myself,' he went on, 'deep inside. I *know* I can do anything if I just get the chance. Think back to when you were my age. Remember how you felt when you went after that first job? Remember how you

30

wanted to prove yourself — how you wanted that job so desperately that you couldn't sleep the night before the interview? Then remember how crushed you were when the guy said: "What experience have you had?"'

Brantley wasn't even mindful of his audience now; he was like a jazz musician doing a riff on self-confidence, blowing out note after note of inner faith.

'You just wanted to shake your fists at the world and shout, "I can do anything — somebody give me a chance!"'

Brantley dropped his horn; he settled back, exhausted, in his chair. He did not even notice that his audition had succeeded: both of his Uncle's eyebrows were raised now and not with mockery.

Just then, Maureen entered the room.

'They're ready for you in the boardroom, Mr Prescott,' she said. She gave a quizzical glance at the depleted Brantley before she moved to leave again.

'Wait a minute,' Prescott said, before she did. 'Call Bates in Personnel. Tell him I'm sending someone down.'

Maureen smiled, glad. She winked at Brantley — who sat straight up on hearing — then left the office.

Brantley beamed out his most astonished grin. Maybe if he waited long enough, his Uncle would even say 'spunk.'

Prescott said something more realistic, however. 'You're in the front door. What you do on this side of it is up to you.'

Brantley nodded. That was okay with him. Everything was okay with him now.

It may not have mattered that kin was kin. What mattered was that Brantley was Brantley.

CHAPTER FOUR

He didn't start out as Vice-President.

He didn't start out as an executive, an executive assistant or even as a male secretary. Brantley was sent to the place fabled in song and story, the place that had come to represent the dregs, the dumps, the bog from which workers either ascend or are sucked under for good.

The mailroom.

Pemrose Inc's mailroom fully satisfied Brantley's expectations. It was a jammed, cacophonous area in which a dozen workers — ten too many for the space — scrambled, shouted, dodged or bashed into each other in their attempt to facilitate the flow of correspondence. Cigarette smoke permeated the air; obscenities were the most commonly heard form of speech; sweat, cigars and rubber cement were the place's perfumes.

Brantley was undisturbed — that is, after the initial sinking feeling and shock he had experienced. With a mischievous smile, the Personnel officer had asked, 'You know where you'll be working, don't you?' Brantley *had* hoped the answer would be, 'At the top.' But this joke had two punchlines and the man had chosen the other one.

Now he felt there was a certain amount of poetic justice to it, though poetry was the last thing that came to mind in the mailroom. He felt his beginnings would be so typically humble that his ascension would have to be typically dazzling. The mailroom was to a job what his apartment was to a home: an incentive.

As he looked at the cursing, scurrying mailroom employees, as he tried to fight through the mob to meet his boss, he thought, this is a long way from KRS, Inc.

In the distance, through a maze of packages and people, stamps and stampedes, he saw the little cubicle in which his superior dwelled. The subway had taught him ways to maneuver in situations like this: elbows out, he twisted his way through the crowd to freedom.

'Freedom' seemed ironic, however, when he saw Barney Brady's place of business. Two perfunctory walls separated it from the rest of the tumultuous mailroom. It looked like the solitary confinement area of a very lax prison. Everyone in New York lived and worked in cells, Brantley thought. Somehow, *he* would make a break for it.

Right now, there was Brady to meet. And to survive meeting.

He was a heavyset man in his early forties. Deep semicircles cupped his eyes; his hair had long ago fled from his head. He wore no jacket or tie but it did not make him seem informal, merely uncivilized. Brantley looked down self-consciously at his own fancy attire, his one blue suit. So did Brady.

'Hey, Bozo,' he said, 'you can't come in here. Take your crap to the mail slot.'

Brantley savored this mistake for a minute; for a fleeting second, he felt like an executive. Then sighing deeply, he forced himself to correct Barney Brady and accept the consequences.

'I work here,' he managed to say. 'Just starting.'

Brantley tentatively held out the memo he had been given by Personnel. Brady's eyes lighted. He made no effort to reach the few feet to retrieve the paper. Instead he smiled, very coldly.

Then he snapped his fingers.

Mortified, obedient, Brantley shuffled over the few offending feet. When he stopped, Brady smiled again, to say Very Good. Then impatiently he snatched the memo from Brantley's hands.

When he had finished reading it, he snorted, with disbelief.

'Brantley?' he said. 'Brantley? Somebody *gave* you that name? Oh, Jesus.' He looked up, having pegged this kid now. 'A college puke. This really makes my day.'

'You're welcome,' Brantley said. He wished to add that it had been a stupid name even before he went to college but stayed silent.

Brady kept shaking his head, laughing quietly. Then he lifted his head suddenly and barked out across the mailroom.

'Melrose! Get over here!'

Brady turned back to Brantley. 'Listen to what this guy tells you, then do what he does. Stay out of my way, don't use the stamp machine for personal letters.' He gave Brantley one last withering once-over. 'And take off that stupid-looking tie. It looks like you shot your couch. Any questions?'

Clearing his throat, abashedly, Brantley said nothing. He simply started to loosen his tie.

'What do I call you?' he asked, finally.

Brady grinned, glad he asked. 'Call me God.'

Fred Melrose approached then. He was a lean thirty-four-year-old with a friendly face and a perpetually skeptical look. Though Brady had hollered for him, Melrose had taken his own sweet time about arriving.

'You got a problem, boss?' he asked, with subtle satire. 'I'm your man.'

Brady was oblivious of Melrose's attitude. 'Show this college puke the ropes and keep him out of my face. His name is . . . ' he puckered up, as if to spit, 'Brantley.'

Melrose started his lesson not in the mailroom but in the executive suite. They left the elevator on the thirty-ninth floor and walked down the plush, silent corridors. Brantley felt a terrible yearning, like a man staring at an

35

unattainable woman.

'Twice a day,' Melrose began, 'you deliver here like a mailman and pick up whatever is going out. I can do it in thirty minutes,' he confided, grinning, 'Brady thinks it takes me two hours.'

'What department is this?' Brantley asked, wistfully. 'What do they do up here?'

'Who knows?' Melrose shrugged. 'This place is a zoo. Nobody knows what anybody else is doing.'

Brantley was interested in this last piece of information. There seemed something hopeful about it, somehow; he was not sure why. Perhaps in a place where there was no organization, anything could happen.

This possibility made Brantley smile. He was still smiling when an executive passed him and threw him a scowl in response.

'Hey,' Melrose said. 'Not the suits. Never consort with the suits unless they consort with you first.'

Brantley was taken aback. If anything, he felt less at ease 'consorting' with Melrose. 'That's ridiculous. He's a person, I'm a person. I can't smile and nod "hello"?'

'He's not a person. He's a suit. No consorting.'

As they rounded a corner, Melrose suddenly shushed him. The older mailroom worker walked stealthily now, as if through a minefield.

'We're entering a sensitive zone,' he whispered. 'The guy in the next office just got canned. The mailroom knew about it Friday. He found out today.'

'Is his job still open?' Brantley asked, hopefully.

Melrose shook his head. 'The job was dissolved. Economic cutbacks. About two dozen suits got the axe.'

Brantley couldn't help himself. He slowed down near the fired executive's office and peeked in. A man with his head bent was slowly and mournfully cleaning out his desk.

Melrose grabbed his arm then. 'Will you quit trying to consort?'

It was a long lesson from Melrose. It was a long day in general. Brantley Foster, mailroom worker, rode the elevator to the lobby exhausted.

When he got out, he felt positively wilted. His good shirt was sweated through, his jacket was slung carelessly over his back, wrinkling more every minute. Brantley shrugged, sadly. What difference did it make? What did appearance mean to a mailroom worker?

He slunk across the lobby, his posture and gait in direct contrast to his formerly confident stride. He stopped at a water fountain. He let the water hit his face, as if to wash it off, as if to cleanse the very idea of the mailroom from him.

Then he turned and saw her.

There was still water in his eyes; his vision was still blurred. He saw her as if through a waterfall, as if he were a satyr and she a nymph.

A nymph in a three-piece suit, however. Clutching her briefcase, she let her long legs carry her ever closer across the lobby. Her blonde hair was impeccably coiffed, swinging just above her shoulders. She was about twenty-five yet seemed already to have achieved an executive position. She was the epitome of the day's successful female. Wonder Woman. Supergirl.

She was beautiful.

She was also thirsty. She looked at Brantley expectantly. He was hovering over the fountain, dumbstruck, staring at her. She raised her eyebrows, waiting for him to move.

'Excuse me,' she said.

Brantley couldn't hear her. He couldn't hear anything; his heart was thumping in his ears, deafening him.

'Excuse me,' she said again.

This time, her words managed to carry through the sound of his pulsing blood. He nodded. Then he did more than let her drink. He turned on the water and let it rise high before her. She looked at him, strangely, not

37

knowing whether or not to be flattered. Then she shrugged. She bent over and dipped her lips into the spray.

He watched, thrilled, as the water slapped lightly against her lips. He did not blink, so as not to miss it entering her mouth, sliding along her tongue. He watched her throat move as she swallowed.

She pulled back then. She dabbed off her lips with a finger. Then she gave him only the slightest of nods.

'Thank you,' she said.

She said it as she might to a doorman holding her packages for her; as she might to a delivery boy handing her back a receipt. As she might to a mailroom worker.

Brantley watched her as she turned and walked away. He watched her slim body course swiftly, gracefully through the crowded lobby. He watched as a pen — from her briefcase? from her inside coat pocket? — fell slowly and hit the floor.

Brantley immediately sprang forward. Bending, he pushed other workers out of the way, his eyes fixed on the pen, like a skateboard beggar sliding after dropped change. At last, he had it; he scooped it up.

He turned; the mystery woman was already revolving out of the revolving doors. He ran, waving the pen, as if holding up his heart for her to see.

He got as far as the doors. Through them, through the revolving forms of other, less important people, he saw her purposefully approach the curb. There a cab, like a coach in a fairy tale, awaited her. Beside the cab was, unfortunately, Prince Charming: a young and handsome executive. To Brantley's joy, they only spoke for a second. Then she got into the cab alone.

As she did, two profound events occurred. First, in maneuvering herself inside, she revealed the top of a creamy, stockinged thigh. Second, she glanced back at the building.

Was it telepathy on her part? Brantley did not care. He

only knew that in that instant, their eyes met.

She looked at him a second; there was no mistaking it; she looked at *him*, not the building, and at no one else. Then she whipped both legs inside the cab and stared straight ahead. Then she was gone.

That night, Brantley applied himself to finishing a paint job on his apartment walls. As he slopped the white stuff on and smoothed it out, he could not help but think of the white skin of that woman. He applied the paint with long, loving strokes.

Then he stood back and looked at his handiwork. Between the plants and the pictures and the paint job, it was starting to look like a presentable place: a place a man could bring a beautiful young executive.

Then he heard the sounds of sex.

For a minute, he thought maybe it was his *own* heavy breathing. But no, the sounds of moans, cries and powerful bed banging was coming in through his freshly painted walls. It was as if his imagination had been manifested.

This gave him less pleasure than it was obviously giving the people next door. In fact, the very absence of such activity in his own room — in his own life — could not have been made more obvious. He tried to drown it out by singing to himself. But there was no escaping it.

Finally, he began conducting. His hands flying up like Leonard Bernstein's, he directed the cries, the sighs, the crashes. He orchestrated their pleasure, the way he intended to orchestrate his own . . . somehow.

CHAPTER FIVE

In the mailroom, Brantley tried hard to learn.

Not about delivering mail: that he left to the employees at his left and right, whizzing letters into various slots, pressing stamps onto Jiffy bags, tying string around boxes. *He* tried hard to learn what was behind the interoffice memos — some of them marked 'Confidential' — that fell into his hot hands on the way to their destinations.

This meant, of course, that while his colleagues sent their letters and parcels off quickly and efficiently — fueled by their fear of Brady — Brantley's progress often slowed to a stop. It took him awhile to read the memos, after all.

Melrose noticed. Protectively, he tried to warn Brantley.

'You're supposed to deliver them, not read them,' he said.

Brantley couldn't get over it. He slapped the memo in his hand, exasperatedly. 'But some of these things don't make sense. They send requisitions through two different departments to get procurements for a third. What kind of thinking is that?'

'Suit thinking. Something happens to a man when he puts on a neck-tie. It cuts off the oxygen to his brain.'

Someone not wearing a tie — but not known for his intelligence, either — now appeared behind them. Brady loomed up like a wave at Brantley's left shoulder.

'Hey, you — college puke!'

This was now officially his name. Brantley replied, instinctively.

'Yo!'

'Get your ass in gear or I'll ship you back to Princeton!'

'Kansas State, sir!'

This kind of correction was not appreciated by Brady, to whom all colleges were equally awful. He jutted his face close to Brantley's. Suddenly, he was not in a corporation but in a Marine training camp.

'Do you like it here, Foster?' Sergeant Brady bellowed.

'Love it, sir!' Brantley, the maggot, answered.

'Then you'd better show some fast improvement, boy. I never went to college — never had any advantages — but I know how to sort mail into boxes.'

'Remarkable,' Brantley said, sincerely.

As usual, sarcasm went right over Brady's head, not high to begin with. 'I'm watching you, Foster. Every moment, God is watching.' Brady could not help but notice Melrose watching, amusedly. 'You, too, Melrose — move it!'

Brantley moved. He moved straight to his daily rounds, which included scoping out the thirty-ninth floor, lair of the executives.

As he pushed his mail cart, he made sure to move with pleasant optimism, saying hello to all — even the dreaded 'suits' — and smiling at the secretaries. At least they smiled back at the cute young mailroom worker.

One woman did not smile back. She did not even notice him; she was too busy talking to a group of executives. It was she, the beautiful girl from the lobby, the businesswoman of his dreams.

As she passed, Brantley tried to pick up whatever he could of her conversation. He managed to hear something extremely important: her name.

Christy. Christy Welles.

What a name, he thought, as he almost rammed his

42

mail cart absently into the wall. It was perfect: Christy, like crystal, a shiny, special commodity. Welles, like a well, deep and filled with sustenance. Christy, like Christie Brinkley, a great beauty. Welles, like Orson Welles, a great genius.

Lost in his reverie, Brantley did not realize that he was not alone. Melrose was at his side now, following Brantley's gaze. Brantley turned and started from the surprise of seeing him. Then he merely melted.

'She's the most incredible-looking woman I've ever seen in my life,' he said.

Melrose had to give him that. 'Yeah. She's a Rolls Royce. But she's also a suit.'

'What's she like? What do you know about her?'

'I know enough never to consort with the suits — even when they have legs like hers.'

Her leg: Brantley saw it again getting into the cab. The kind of leg that could confer greatness on a man. He was greedy for information now. 'Come on. You know more than that.'

Melrose shrugged. 'She's supposed to be some sort of financial wizard. Harvard and all that crap.'

Brantley's stare became even more avid as he heard the name of Christy's Alma Mater. A body like that *and* Harvard Business School. A combination like that could rule the world. And him.

'Hey,' Melrose said, impatiently now, 'forget it!'

But you don't forget something like that. Melrose thought he would have to pull Brantley back before he headed into deeper waters. Sharks lay in wait there; and beautiful or not, sharks were sharks.

Melrose was even more disturbed when he had lunch with Brantley. The two of them sat outside in the sun at Citicorp Plaza. Melrose had a brown bag with a tuna fish sandwich in it. Brantley had a handful of memos.

'Hey,' Melrose said, 'what are you, crazy? You're not supposed to take memos out of the mailroom.'

43

But Brantley had the same possessed look he had when watching Christy. He hardly even registered Melrose's complaint.

'I can't follow a chain of command in this company,' Brantley said, frustratedly, fanning the memos. 'They've all got the right title but their job objectives and assignments are all screwed up. Look at Purchasing — it's a mess. They've got two people doing basically the same job and neither is doing it right.'

Melrose glanced around, on the lookout for any approaching suits. 'Yeah, well, I'll bring it up at the next stockholders' meeting. Will you put those things away?'

But Brantley just kept reading them, lost in his own world. This kid may be too smart for his own good, Melrose thought; or he was just too stupid to be afraid. Either attitude could spell disaster in business. Or triumph.

Brady was about to give Brantley his first shot at one or the other.

CHAPTER SIX

It happened the next day. Brantley was busy reading memos and watching other people sort mail. Melrose was busy watching out for Brantley. Brady was talking on the phone.

'What?' he was saying. 'Look, that's Transportation's problem. We don't supply drivers for execs' wives. We're a messenger service. I don't care if all the drivers are busy. Yeah, same to you, buddy.'

Brady hung up. Then he sat stewing for a second, big angry clouds floating up from his cigar. He turned, still brooding. Then he saw Brantley. A cruel smiled crossed his lips.

'Hey, Dartmouth — get over here!'

By now, Brantley knew to respond to any insulting nickname. Tearing himself away from a particularly interesting memo, he approached his superior.

'Look,' Brady said, 'an executive's wife needs a ride out to Litchfield. Check out a car and drive her.'

Brantley was not amused. Mailroom was one thing; he could at least read memos there. But chauffeuring!

'Where's Litchfield?' he asked, clearly irritated.

'You'll find out,' Brady replied. 'Just follow the smell of money.'

Brantley sat in the car, impatiently waiting outside the Pemrose building. The car was at an even temperature; it was the driver who was over-heating.

It'd probably be some old, fat lady with a fox around her neck, he thought, annoyed. She'd treat him like some sort of 'hired man,' as she might her butler or her caddy. It would be a long ride to Litchfield.

Then the old, fat, rich lady got in.

There was no doubt that she was rich; old or fat she was not.

She was instead about forty, extremely svelte, extremely cool and extremely sexy. Brantley stared amazed into the rearview mirror.

'Excuse me, ma'am,' he said. 'I'm not quite sure which —'

Her reply was curt. 'Go left.'

Brantley went left. As he did, weaving his way in and out of midtown traffic, his eyes kept darting to the rearview mirror. The woman sat, her fingers with their long red nails tapping angrily on the armrest, her eyes staring furiously out the window. He was about to ask if there was anything he could do to help when she told him what he could do.

'Put on some music.'

Brantley immediately complied. His fingers flipped nervously through the possible choices: country-western, disco, rap, oldies. He passed heavy metal.

'Leave that on,' the woman said.

Brantley's eyebrows rose. 'You like heavy metal?'

'I hate it.'

Brantley did as he was told. They moved along in silence for awhile. Brantley couldn't help but notice her wince with what seemed pleasure as the brutal chords of heavy metal struck her ears. He felt a little sorry for her. He felt a lot of lust and a little sorry. It was enough to provoke him to speak.

'I know I'm not supposed to consort and all . . . '

'What?' she snapped.

'You — seem very upset. Is there anything I can do to . . . '

'You could find me a brick.'

'A brick?'

46

'To drop on my husband's balls.'

Brantley nodded, a bead of sweat falling down his face. Just shut up and drive, he thought. Drive along. A nice, long, silent drive.

They crossed a bridge, Brantley listening uncomfortably to more of Ozzy Osbourne's screaming. The woman had begun to move her head a little as if in rhythm to the tuneless music. Brantley had to keep snapping his eyes back to the road in order not to kill them both.

At last, she snapped up the phone in the back of the car. She pushed out the number as if stabbing someone. Then she picked off an earring and held the receiver to her ear.

Brantley leaned his head back onto the headrest to hear her conversation. He missed a few greetings and endearments. Then she got to the good stuff.

'Does he think I'm an idiot? This is the third weekend he's managed not to come to the country. I know he's screwing around with some teenage airhead from the steno pool.'

Brantley had leaned back so far that he was practically sitting on the backseat. The woman noticed. She held the receiver against her chest. She looked witheringly at him.

The straining Brantley had not noticed she had noticed. She gave him a clue.

'Do you know my husband?' she asked, suddenly.

Brantley was startled. He immediately sprang forward and practically pressed himself against the wheel. 'Ma'am?'

The woman only snorted out a contemptuous laugh. 'Never mind.'

'I didn't hear a thing,' Brantley said, his nose almost on the windshield.

Shaking her head, the executive's wife went back to her conversation, which she soon ended.

After she was done, she tapped a bit more on the armrest. Then she pulled a compact from her bag. She

47

began carefully applying make-up. Brantley watched her in his mirror as she watched herself in her own. She was paying particular attention to a wrinkle she believed to be near her eye. There's nothing there, Brantley wished to tell her; you look great.

She spoke then, casually, informally, as if Brantley were a confidante. 'It makes me absolutely furious. He looks twice as good as he did the day we were married. I just look twice as old.'

There was a touch of kittenish pouting in her voice. Brantley could not resist telling her the truth — which was also what she obviously wished to hear.

'Are you kidding?' he said. 'You look . . . well, when I'm his age, I hope I can wake up every morning and find a woman as beautiful as you there beside me.'

There was a pause. Then the woman raised her eyes slowly from the mirror. She met Brantley's eyes in his mirror. He stopped at a light.

They stared at each other for a minute. Then Brantley noticed one of her red-taloned hands pressing down her door lock.

They were shut inside now, locked as if in a hothouse, as if in a steamroom; Brantley had to wipe his brow. Instinctively, he reached out and did what any young man might do.

He opened all the doors.

Brantley pressed down on the 'Door lock' button the way pilots do on seat ejections. He breathed a little easier.

The woman only shrugged. She took out her lipstick, rolled it to a fat point and rubbed it around her lips. Then she put something else in her mouth: a long cigarette from which she sucked.

Brantley hit a switch and the divider went up.

The glass wasn't entirely to the roof of the car, separating them, when the woman pressed her own finger onto her own switch. The glass slowly went down again.

Brantley smiled weakly at her in the rearview mirror. She smiled more pointedly back. Her smile began to grow more amorous.

Brantley hit his window switch and his window went down. Then he tried to correct it; the woman's window went down. The windows were flying up and down, like pants and skirts, sweaters and chemises, before and after, before and after.

They arrived at the woman's home.

CHAPTER SEVEN

It was more than a home: it was a mansion, it was a palace. It was a large Georgian place hidden behind gates. Brantley had to cruise up what seemed a quarter of a mile driveway before he reached the front.

When he got there, he merely sat at the wheel, the motor idling, gawking. It took the woman opening her door to snap him out of it.

She started slowly towards the house, leaving her packages on the seat behind her.

'Bring those inside,' she told him.

Brantley obeyed. Two packages under each arm, he shuffled his way up the immaculate path to the fancy front door.

Once inside, he was directed to a large back room that took Brantley's breath away. It held a bar made of mahogany wood, a working fireplace and glass walls that looked out on a tennis court and pool. Brantley managed to mask his amazement behind an imitation of nonchalance. He carefully laid down the packages.

The woman — on the phone he had heard her call herself Vera — crossed immediately to the bar. She began dropping ice cubes into glasses.

'What are you drinking?' she asked, brusquely.

'I have to drive back,' Brantley stammered.

Vera took this to mean Vodka. She poured two drinks, handed one swiftly to him. Then she moved to the glass wall and looked silently out at the tennis court and the pool. She sighed.

'God, I hate the country,' she said. 'Who can live with so many trees?'

'Yeah,' Brantley said, with a slight smile. 'I can see how you'd be really miserable here . . .'

She paid him no mind. 'And beginning tomorrow, the army moves in — caterers, florists, bartenders, waiters, maids. And *why*? For the branch managers from Akron and Joplin and Mobile! And while the men talk business, I get to be with the women who only talk about the men's business.'

She spoke as if there were no choice and would never be any change. She sardonically clinked her glass against his.

'Here's to corporate life.'

She downed her drink in practically one swallow. Though Brantley was still uneasily nursing his, Vera moved back to the bar.

'Have another,' she said.

She swiftly poured more Vodka into his glass. Brantley gave a great sigh as her liquid splashed over his cubes. Then she turned away again and turned her attention back outside.

'I've run eight thousand miles on that tennis court, chasing a ball with a racket.' She turned back then. 'Do my legs look heavy to you?'

'God, no!' Brantley said, quickly.

This seemed to please Vera. She smiled a bit, swiveling back to her backyard. 'I've swum laps from here to the moon in that pool. You see anything that's not firm?'

Brantley was practically guzzling his drink now. His eyes scanned Vera's body for any possible signs of flab. None present.

'Tennis, swimming, anything to stay in shape — not that he would ever notice. Do you see anything wrong with me?'

It was apparent to her from Brantley's eyes that he did not. There was an aching, pleading quality in her voice that was giving him chills. It was as if she were pouring her drink slowly down his back.

'Maybe the only thing wrong with you,' he said, 'is that your husband's just a jerk.'

Vera started from this remark. It was both insolent and encouraging, insulting and kind. She hadn't been ready for it. Now she clearly was ready. The question was, as her eyes bore into him: was he?

'I really have to get back,' Brantley said, in answer. 'Brady already hates me for going to college.'

Vera moved to stop him then. She did not throw herself across the door or attach herself to his ankles. She merely, with a limp hand, picked up the telephone.

'Transportation, please,' she said, after dialing. 'The young man from the mailroom who drove me home is going to stay here and mow the lawn. See that he gets full credit on his time card.'

She smiled and hung up. Then, very calmly, she addressed Brantley. 'How about a dip in the pool?'

Brantley sighed. He was hot. She was hot. It was hot. It was going to be a day for conjugating.

Brantley borrowed a bathing suit which was meant for a man much heftier than he. He had to tie it several times with the little cord before it fit his smaller waist.

He stood on the diving board as reticent as a child about jumping in. Then, never much of a swimmer anyway, he merely moved his feet off the board's end and found the rest of him followed.

He sank beneath the surface of the water. When he bobbed to the top again, he saw Vera perched like a beautiful, predatory bird upon the board.

Her suit was sleek and tight and revealed a figure of which any young woman would have been proud. She spread her arms, arched her back, and flew up in a perfect dive. She cut cleanly into the water beside him.

'I swim five miles a day,' she said when she resurfaced. 'It's supposed to tone my ass.'

'It works,' Brantley said, helplessly.

Vera laughed at him. Then suddenly she disappeared beneath the water again. There was a pause in which Brantley merely stood, squinting into the sun.

Then he felt a tug on his suit.

It was a hard tug; then it grew into a yank. He felt his suit passing from his torso to his ankles.

Brantley thrashed, fighting her. But she seemed to be everywhere, arms, legs, hands, feet. He felt like a diver battling an octopus and losing. The strain of the battle brought Vera to the surface.

'This is crazy!' Brantley said.

What was crazy was that Brantley was nude. What was crazier was that Vera was getting the same way, discarding her top.

'I know we're taking a terrible chance,' she said, 'but I know the owner.'

'You know,' Brantley said, reasonably, 'I think it would be better if . . . '

He was given no chance to be reasonable. In a second, he was under water again, squirming out of seduction like a fish fleeing a hook. They both rose to the air again, panting.

'My husband could be home any minute,' she said, 'or several hours from now.'

Brantley grew pale. 'Oh my God. Husband roulette.'

Vera took two little steps. She looked him right in the eye. Then her bikini bottom came up and floated, like someone exhausted, someone giving in.

Like Brantley Foster.

It was a lot easier in the house. First of all, it was inside. Second of all, it was not flooded with water. Lastly, it had a bed, which always comes in handy when you are being seduced by an older woman.

Afterwards, Brantley lay on the enormous divan, sighing. Who *was* this woman? What was her last name? These questions passed idly into his brain and out again.

Here, at last, was his first real adventure in the big city. If it had had nothing to do with money, if it had had nothing to do with love, well, there would be plenty of time for all that.

Now he wished to merely savor the afterglow of his first illicit encounter. An older woman. A married woman. A woman who now stood bare before a mirror at the bar, fiddling with her hairdo.

'I'm going to see to it that my husband helps you advance at Pemrose,' she said.

'Thanks,' Brantley said, 'but I've got plans. This company doesn't know it yet, but it needs me. I'm going to move up without anyone's help.'

Vera smiled. 'Oh, God, you're cute.'

She rejoined him on the divan. She lay next to him, bracing herself with one elbow. She studied his face. She traced it with a forefinger, as if marveling at his lack of lines.

'I could spend a week inside those eyes,' she said.

Brantley smiled. No one had ever said anything that corny to him before. 'If you don't mind a personal observation . . .'

'Brantley, we're both naked. You can say anything you want to.'

'Well . . . you got off the track somewhere along the way. Somebody sold you a bill of goods and convinced you that you have to be twenty-one forever. I think you're terrific. You're intelligent, you're sensual and you're beautiful.'

The words were like sex to Vera. 'Say that again.'

Brantley was about to express more excited compliments when he heard a noise. Besides a nuclear blast, it was the last thing any man sleeping with someone else's wife wants to hear.

He heard a car pulling into the driveway.

'Oh, no,' Vera said.

Both of them scrambled across the room to look out.

They saw a Cadillac stop and turn off in the driveway.
They saw the door open. Then they saw a man get out.
  Brantley's Uncle Howard.

CHAPTER EIGHT

'My husband!' Vera said.

'My uncle!' Brantley said.

Vera turned slowly and looked at him. 'Your *what*?'

Brantley just stared at her. 'Then you're . . . '

'Aunt Vera?' Aunt Vera said.

'Oh, Christ!'

Brantley immediately bolted from her. He dived into a pile of discarded clothes, searching for his own.

'What's my mother gonna say?' he mumbled. 'I've disgraced the entire family!'

Brantley could see the headlines now. 'Mailroom Worker Killed by Irate Uncle'; 'Incest Nips Promising Lad's Career in Bud.'

But Vera was having no such nightmares. She was laughing.

Brantley stopped dressing for a second. 'No,' he said. 'Not funny. This is not a funny moment in my life.'

'Stop panicking,' she said. 'Who's going to find out?'

Brantley turned. Prescott's footsteps were ever more quickly approaching the house.

'I'm home!' Prescott called.

'*He's* going to find out,' Brantley said, pulling on his socks.

'Don't worry,' Vera said, still amused. 'He won't fire you.'

'There is no way he's gonna give me a raise for this.'

Brantley scooted up the stairs then, his shirt still unbuttoned to his navel. He was halfway up when, outside, he heard a significant question from Prescott.

'Vera? What's the company car doing in the driveway?'

Brantley stopped. 'Oh, my God . . . ' How could he have been so stupid? What did he think would happen if he slept with an executive's wife, relative or no? Did he think he would just get away with it? Pemrose was a huge company but it was still a small town.

He continued up the stairs as he heard Vera's clever but completely inconvenient reply.

'It broke down. The boy who drove me home had to take the train back to town.'

Brantley bent over the railing for a last whisper to Vera. 'How *am* I gonna get back to town?'

Vera looked up, with high hilarity. 'Maybe we'll just keep you here and adopt you.'

With that, Brantley bolted for the terrace. Hearing the knob turn downstairs, he held his breath and took one great leap over. At the exact moment he was in the air, Prescott was in the house.

Uncle Howard had found his wife lolling naked on the divan. Brantley heard what he could as he grew airborne.

'What the hell are you doing in here?'

'Feeling romantic,' Vera said.

'Oh. Dinner ready?'

'Oh, Howard. You really know how to sweep a girl back up on her feet.'

Brantley landed in the center of some brambles. Right on his ankle.

Pain shooting up his lower leg, he lay in the thorns, nursing his wound, hearing the mild arguing of Prescott and Vera. She's enjoying this, he thought, resentfully. What a woman and what a world.

Brantley tried to stand. He figured if he ever got out of this alive, he would have a nifty story to tell his grandchildren. Of course, he might have to clean it up a little. This prospect made him laugh.

Then he heard someone who was not so amused.

Some*thing*, to be exact. Human beings do not growl in so horrifying a way. When Brantley turned, he saw what seemed a big black horse looking at him with bared fangs.

Horses don't have fangs, Brantley thought. But dogs do. Dobermans.

He had one choice. Either he could remain still, refusing to irritate his ankle, and be eaten. Or he could further enflame his leg, try to run, and survive.

Brantley looked across the lawn to a large glass greenhouse. That was his safe haven, his harbor in the storm. Stomping agonizingly on his injured foot, he took off.

I'll get Brady for this, he thought.

The Doberman yapping at his heels, he flew across the tapered lawn to the greenhouse front door. He pulled the door frantically open. Then he practically slammed it on the animal's gaping mouth.

He stood, panting, flat up against the door, pressing it shut with his back. Pain traveled from his ankle up his leg into his shoulder and to his brain. He heard the animal panting and scratching outside, kicking one horsey leg against the door. Better Uncle Howard's dog than Uncle Howard himself, Brantley thought.

Then he heard Uncle Howard himself.

'Duke! You got another rabbit cornered, boy?'

Brantley felt faint. Yes, that's right, he thought, he's got another rabbit. Someone who did it like a bunny and would now be killed like one. He heard his Uncle Howard's approaching feet crunch the grass of the lawn.

'Get me out of this, Lord,' Brantley prayed aloud, 'and I promise I'll go all over the world and tell everyone not to screw their boss' wife . . . '

Prescott was getting closer; Brantley could hear him whispering commands to his feverish dog. As soon as his Uncle was visible through the window, Brantley dropped to his hands and knees.

Crawling swiftly through the greenhouse, his palms being stabbed by briers, stained by dirt, he headed for the door at the other end. When he reached it, his hand flew above his head, grappled blindly at the knob. He pulled it open — into his forehead. Cursing quietly, he crawled through into what seemed safety. It was, in reality, an attached tool shed.

It was pitch black. Brantley rose, cautiously, and immediately knocked loudly into a rake. Then, shushing himself, he took another careful step and bashed into a shovel. Rolling his eyes, rubbing his arm and leg, he moved to a window. He pulled aside a little curtain.

The Doberman was eating the glass.

At least, that's what it looked like. The dog had its salivating mouth only inches away from his face, gnawing at the distance. Brantley screamed and jumped back.

He started towards the greenhouse again. Then he heard Prescott entering it.

He jumped back into the darkness of the tool shed. He found his footing and managed to stand up on a bench, out of sight. His chest heaving, he stood there, hoping to arrange one final ruse.

He stuck his foot out. He placed it on the doorknob of the outside door. Then he turned it.

There was a pause. Then, slowly, sensing a trap, the Doberman entered. The dog sniffed around, sniffed the floor, the tool equipment and was about to sniff Brantley's bench.

Then Prescott knocked over a pot.

The dog's head flew up like a shot. Immediately, the animal darted into the greenhouse and — Brantley assumed, for he could only hear, not see — right for his master's throat.

'Duke!' Prescott screamed. 'No! It's me! Duke! Ahhhh!'

Brantley took this moment to do the humanitarian thing. He high-tailed it out of the toolshed. *He* was a human, too, after all.

As he sped through the backyard, heading for a fence

growing ever closer, he heard Uncle Howard and Duke still duking it out.

CHAPTER NINE

A few hours' sleep did not erase the fatigue from Brantley's face.

When he ran into Melrose the next morning, his colleague did not have to be psychic to sense upset.

'You look like death on a cracker,' Melrose said. 'What happened?'

'I was chased by a dog that weighed two hundred pounds and had a mouth as big as my head. And that was the *best* thing that happened to me last night.'

'What was the worst thing that happened to you last night?'

'I got laid.'

Melrose looked at him. 'I'm not sure you've got your priorities straight, Brantley.'

The two were walking down the executive corridors, mail carts rolling before them. As soon as the talk turned to sex, a person appeared in front of them, as if by magic.

The young businesswoman.

Christy Welles was walking with her usual pack of executives, discussing something lucrative. Brantley could not keep his eyes away from her. He saw Christy Welles and her friends cram themselves into an elevator. He saw her pushed out to the front, equidistant between the doors. Then he saw something else.

He saw her smile at him.

She did so quickly, warmly, as the doors closed upon her. Was it his imagination? He did not think so. All memories of Vera, Vera's husband and Vera's husband's dog disappeared.

'You're watching her again,' Melrose warned.

'That's 'cause I want to go where she's going.'

'She's going up. You're going down — down to the dead end of the mailroom, from which there is no escape.'

Brantley shrugged the words away. 'They've never built a prison that could hold me.'

Still, it was true, they were going down. The next elevator took them in that direction.

Brantley stayed late that night. He stayed long after everyone, even Brady, had gone. With only a radio to keep him company, he worked overtime for free.

The memos were what kept him. He read enough of them now to be able to sort them into piles of varying importance. Then when he had collected the most urgent, the most telling, he took them to the Xerox and made copies for himself.

After the copies were made, he entered them into his own private notebook. It had been divided into company departments. He wrote brief notes on each, then carefully filed them.

He had been busy gathering more and more information. The day before, he had even gone to the Corporate Reference Center on the second floor of Pemrose. He had walked in, looking very harried and very purposeful. Printed materials were piled high on shelf after shelf. Only one clerk manned the whole place.

'Hi,' Brantley had said. 'We've been getting a lot of requests in the mailroom for stockholder info. Company assets, expenditures, anything you can give us.'

He had thought the clerk might be suspicious. But he was more tired and exasperated.

'You kidding?' he had replied. 'Any of this clutter you want, you can have. Take it out of here.'

This was a godsend to Brantley. He immediately went to the shelves and collected anything he could find. His arms piled high, he had nodded his thanks and left.

Now he took all of this information home. He stayed up late into the morning, poring over graphs, charts, rearranging memos. He checked and cross-checked. He wrote queries to himself on pages, answered some questions and left others unresolved.

All of Pemrose was becoming clear to him now. The whole intricate corporate structure was unfolding before his bloodshot eyes.

He closed his eyes then. In the darkness, he saw endless numerals parading before him. He saw letters dancing in a Rockettes chorus line. He saw Vera's body. He saw Christy Welles' smile. And he saw himself, armed with information that was all beginning to make sense.

Brantley opened his eyes.

'It's so obvious,' he said aloud.

Suddenly, everything was. He, a lowly mailroom worker, a newcomer to New York, had the answer to Pemrose's problems. He alone knew what to do about them.

He heard a sound then, a familiar sound. It was the rhythmic pleasure coming from next door again, always at the same early hour, as if an alarm went off every night, initiating sex.

This time, the pleasure was his, too. The three of them were having an orgy.

CHAPTER TEN

The next morning, Prescott was ahead of everybody.

The executive was leading a group of panting underlings, all younger than he, around a track on the Pemrose roof. He took great pride in how he led them — not only in business but in exercise. He could still show these little weasels a thing or two.

It wasn't just a jog, either. These morning workouts were quiz sessions, as well, verbal exams with the answers always out-of-breath. This morning, the questions were all-important to their futures.

'Can any of you explain,' Prescott said, his voice steady, 'why our stock is down another quarter point this morning?'

Conspicuously winded, one Art Thomas ventured a weary guess.

'A momentary lapse in the market, Mr Prescott. Nobody's buying.'

'Somebody's buying,' Prescott shot back. 'The transfer sheet shows that somebody's been accumulating an enormous block of our stock.'

'Well, someone is, yes,' Thomas tried to agree, 'but not everyone's buying. That's what I mean.'

'When a stock takes a dive and somebody buys a ton of it —'

'It means the stock is on its way to a quick rebound,' Thomas said, hopefully.

'It means the stock is ripe for a hostile takeover,' Prescott said, flatly.

'And is therefore ripe for a hostile takeover.'

There was a stunned silence on the track now. While panting, all the executives caught their breath. The air turned cold for them. Their feet seemed leaden.

'If somebody mounts a hostile takeover,' Prescott said, 'we'll be standing outside Bloomingdale's selling umbrellas.'

With that, Prescott shot farther ahead. His employees ran after him carrying new burdens.

After the run, the invigorated boss led his staff companions down the hall to his office. Takeovers had been their topic of conversation; takeovers remained their topic.

'I want each of you to examine your department,' Prescott said, 'and determine where we can cut costs.'

Thomas was adamant. 'Right. Cut them to the core.'

'We need to raise capital quickly so we can boost stock support.'

'Exactly. Boost it to the moon.'

Prescott shot an annoyed glance at his most enthusiastic yes-man. Then another employee approached them from the opposite direction.

It was a younger man, a boy, really. When Prescott was face-to-face with him, he finally recognized his own nephew.

'It's me,' Brantley told him, 'Brantley. Kansas. The mail room. I'd like a few minutes to talk to you about some ideas I've —'

'Brantley — right. Good. The mailroom needs new ideas. Put them in a memo.'

'No, I've been able to analyze a few things about the company and . . . '

'Glad to see you,' Prescott said. 'You're looking fine.'

Prescott hurried off with his underlings, leaving Brantley stranded, expectantly, in the hall.

He sighed, all of his new computations and conclusions completely ignored. He watched as his uncle and his lackies disappeared in the distance. Maybe Uncle Howard wanted to hear some ideas about his *wife*, Brantley thought, bitterly.

Then he turned. Before him was an office, the office he remembered he saw vacated on his first day. There was no depressed executive in it now; it was as bare, white and eerily quiet as the moon.

From a sudden impulse, Brantley entered the place now. There was something comforting about being in an office, armed as he was with the information to get him one. Why hadn't Prescott even stopped to listen? he wondered, frustratedly.

He walked farther into the place. He saw what amounted to a skeleton office: a clean desk with a telephone and empty trays, a filing cabinet, bare book shelves, a few small stacks of basic office forms. It was so empty, so elemental, that it encouraged him to fantasize: it was a 'Let's Pretend' office.

Brantley eased himself into the chair behind the desk. He adjusted it for maximum comfort. Then he leaned back and put his feet up on the desk. He looked out the window at the 'medium-status' view of Manhattan. He smiled with satisfaction. Mr Foster was about to start his day.

Then the telephone rang.

Brantley looked at it, astonished. He stared at it as it continued to sound. Finally, after its fifth ring, he picked it up.

'Yeah,' he said, nervously. 'Hello?'

The voice on the other end was impatient. 'Tucker — where have you been all this time? We've got us a problem in Midwest distribution. What're you going to do about it?'

Brantley held his breath for a minute. For that time, he was suspended, held between actions; it was easier that way. When he let out the breath, he knew he would have to act, either hang up or respond. The choice was unbearable.

Then he looked slowly around the bare office again. And he decided to pretend even more: there were his plants, the pictures of his family; in the outside office, his secretary waited. Mr Foster was on top of it. Even if he did have to say he was Mr Tucker.

'What's the problem?' Brantley said.

'Oh, nothing much,' the voice replied, sarcastically. 'We've just got sixty-eight tons of materials going out to Missouri, and the trucking line is putting a gun to our heads. They say they won't carry more than twelve tons in each truck, and that means we have to rent five trucks instead of three. I can't get anyone's approval for the extra two trucks.'

Brantley thought about it for a minute. The solution seemed simple. Was he brave enough to suggest it?

'Tucker? What are you gonna do about it?'

'What does a boxcar cost?' Brantley asked, finally.

'What are you, nuts? Twice as much, at least.'

'Missouri needs the materials, doesn't it? Rent a boxcar.'

There was a pause.

'You'll put that in writing?' the voice asked.

'Sure. Tell the trucking company we have to service our customers. And if they're not going to help us, we'll find somebody who will.'

'Well, all right!' the voice exclaimed. 'That's what we need — some gutsy decisions around here. I'll get back to you.'

Brantley heard the other end click off. He grinned at the simplicity of the whole experience. Then he picked up one of the memo page forms from his desk and put it into 'his' typewriter. He started to type an order for renting a boxcar.

Before he could finish, the phone rang again.

Brantley Tucker answered. 'Hello?'

The voice on the other end was elated. 'Hey, pal — forget the boxcar. The trucking company broke down like a two-dollar watch. They're sending three trucks. The next beer's on me, okay?'

'Okay,' Brantley smiled.

Brantley hung up again. He looked around, awestruck at his own maneuver. He tapped a pencil pensively on the top of 'his' desk. Then he had a new, most audacious idea.

If they would not listen to him — indeed even acknowledge him — as Brantley Foster, he would have to not *be* Brantley Foster.

He would have to iron his blue suit again.

CHAPTER ELEVEN

The next morning, wearing his blue suit, Brantley Foster came out of the subway near Citicorp. Dissolved into a mass of identical executives, he did not stick out and he did not wish to. The army of go-getters marched towards their fortress and target, Pemrose Consolidated.

Standing near them was a mailroom worker.

Melrose stood, checking his watch with annoyance. He usually met Brantley at the subway at exactly this hour. He could not understand why he was late. He could not know that Brantley was walking by him at that moment, disguised as an executive.

Brantley had passed his first test.

The next exam took place in the elevator. Brantley stood there, crushed among his 'colleagues' as the doors closed and the car climbed. An executive on his right and an executive on his left began a conversation.

'Did you see what our stock is doing in *The Wall Street Journal*?' the right man said.

'Down another quarter,' said the left.

'That's almost a full point since Tuesday.'

The two paused. Then Brantley realized they were both staring at the man in between them. They were waiting for Brantley to join in.

Brantley did. 'Uh . . . guess that's why they gave us stock instead of money for a Christmas bonus.'

Brantley smiled at the two and immediately turned his attention elsewhere. From his right and left, he heard murmurs of 'I didn't get a Christmas bonus . . . ' 'Neither did I . . .'

An executive from the back of the car was venturing an opinion on something other than money. 'There's new blood on the sixth floor — a couple of secretaries that'll melt your contacts.'

'They always get them down there,' another complained. 'We get stuck with dogs.' He turned to Brantley. 'How about the women on your floor?'

Brantley shook his head, sadly. 'Like Russian shot putters.'

There was general, depressed agreement at this. Brantley was really feeling his oats now; not a wrong word had come out of his mouth.

'How about those Mets?' someone said.

'Don't get your hopes up,' Brantley told him. 'Good pitching, no hitting. They'll fold in September.'

'No,' somebody else chimed in, 'pitching is half the game.'

'Pitching's the other half,' Brantley said. 'They'll fold.'

A few of them nodded, agreeing with Brantley's wisdom. He got off at 'his' floor, feeling at ease.

He looked down the long corridor, watching out for Brady, Melrose, or anyone else who might actually know him. Then he took the plunge. He strode down the hall, his briefcase waving, whistling quietly. He nodded at passing executives, smiled — more condescendingly — at secretaries. With each step, he gained more confidence. With each step, his stature in the company grew. With each . . .

He saw his Uncle Howard.

Prescott was coming down the hall, chewing out an underling that Brantley knew as Thomas. The other man was nodding, obsequiously, agreeing with the condemnation.

Brantley caught his breath. He looked left and right; he looked behind him for any escape. Then he just darted into the nearest office.

He closed the door quickly behind him. Then he

turned around, breathing a little easier.

It was Christy's office.

She looked up from her desk, with complete surprise. She looked him up and down, as if to say, May I help you? It was clear she did not recognize him.

'Ah,' Brantley said, his heart pounding, 'this isn't the men's room.'

'You're very observant,' she replied, coolly.

Brantley glanced behind him at the door. He heard Prescott's voice still several feet away. He could not leave. He felt the lovely yet cold eyes of Christy on him.

'Nice office,' he said, casually. 'But your — plant is getting a blight on it. You should rotate it towards the sun.'

'Are you the company gardener?'

'No,' Brantley said. Who was he? 'Carlton Whitfield.' What kind of name was *that*? It would have to do. 'I'm new here. Just looking around. How about those Mets?'

Christy looked at him with great annoyance now. He could not help noticing how beautiful she was — and also how ridiculously he was behaving. He heard Prescott's voice fading in the other direction. He quickly opened the door.

'Well,' he said, 'great talking to you. Have a good one.'

Brantley immediately fled her office. Gripping his briefcase, he almost ran, sweating profusely, in the direction of his new 'home.'

'Really swept her off her feet,' he muttered. 'Stupid.'

He found his door and careened through it. The office was just as empty, just as inviting as before.

He quickly went to his desk and opened his briefcase. He took out several blank memos. He looked at them a minute. He looked at the typewriter. He stalled, fearfully, tapping his fingers on the desk, pacing around the room. Then he shrugged.

'Don't look back,' he told himself. 'Be bold.'

75

He sat down at the typewriter, inserted the memos, and typed them out furiously. He sat back and looked at his work. Then Brantley grabbed the telephone.

Closing his eyes for courage, he dialed an extension number. 'Hi. Carlton Whitfield up in 4319. I know you're awfully busy down there but I'm still waiting for the secretary I requested last week. I can't get any letters out, I have to answer my own phone, and it's really becoming a problem. Yes, office 4319.'

There was a pause on the line. Brantley thought he had managed the right tone of piqued self-importance. He waited, then answered an obvious question.

'Empty? Well, that's a mistake. I've been here a week — I've got my name on the door, a desk full of supplies, and my geranium on the window ledge. I've got everything but a secretary. Well, I'll tell you what — I'll have Personnel send a boy down from the mailroom with a requisition order. Thank you.'

Brantley hung up and let out a long breath. Then he clicked open his briefcase. From it, he took the uniform of the 'boy from the mailroom': jeans, T-shirt and a mail apron. He quickly began to remove his suit.

Within a matter of minutes, the person coming out of the empty office was no longer Carlton Whitfield. It was Brantley Foster, mailroom worker. Carrying a handful of newly typed memos, he walked briskly back up the hall. He smiled and nodded at executives again but this time was ignored. Even the secretaries hardly noticed him.

He stopped short at the elevator. Near it, he saw Christy and a few of her male peers getting a cup of coffee from a machine. His head down, he barreled right past her. She never turned to look.

Finally, he reached his destination: the Corporate Staffing Room. He walked in with an underling's annoyance and approached the director, a woman of fifty named Mrs Meachum.

'Big cheese up in 4319 wants his secretary pronto,' Brantley reported.

'Everybody wants something pronto,' world-weary Mrs Meachum replied. 'He'll have to wait.'

'Okay,' Brantley shrugged. 'But I've also got a memo here from 4319 to Prescott about gross inefficiency in the secretarial pool.'

This made Mrs Meachum look up. She glanced at the memo to Prescott that Brantley had laid before her.

'I'll free somebody up within an hour,' she said.

On his way out, Brantley took the Prescott memo which had provoked such respect, crumpled it, and lobbed it into the trash.

Brantley headed next to the Purchasing Department. He walked confidently into the Printing Room. An extremely frantic, overworked clerk looked up at him.

'I've got a memo here that's burning my fingers,' Brantley told him. 'A new suit up in 4319 wants his personalized memos and stationery immediately. I mean, he is hot.'

Brantley chuckled, to imply the depth of this guy's temper. The clerk only looked at him, baffled.

'What? Who?'

'His name is on the memo,' Brantley said. 'He also wants nameplates for his desk and for his door, and he expects them all by noon.'

The clerk looked at him, thoroughly annoyed. Brantley shrugged, as if to say, I don't make the rules. On his way out, he thought with a smile, I do now.

Brantley's next stop should have been his first one: the mailroom. Not pausing long enough to be afraid, he breezed in past Brady. He made to begin his work immediately, but Brady would not let him. He stopped him, rudely, in his tracks.

'You're late,' Brady said.

'I've already done my rounds,' Brantley panted.

Indeed he had; Brantley could not afford to be

anything but ultra-competent now. He dumped his collected mail into a large bin. Then he grinned, innocently, at Brady. The boss was surprised.

'Well, you didn't punch in,' Brady said, stymied.

'I couldn't wait to get to it,' Brantley replied. 'God, I love my work.'

Brantley just stood there, looking efficient and oblivious. Brady could not think of another thing to accuse him of; this frustrated him. So he took the opportunity to shove a large envelope into Brantley's hands.

'Punch in,' he said, 'then run this up to Personnel and wait for an answer.'

'Right,' eager-beaver-Brantley said.

He quickly punched his time card in. Then he hurried out the door to the service elevator, as if hungry for more mailroom work. Brady just watched him, with confused suspicion.

Brantley fulfilled his obligation to Brady. Then he immediately shot back to the office of Carlton Whitfield, newest Pemrose executive.

He quickly entered his inner office. Then he swiftly began to change out of his Brantley costume. He discarded his T-shirt and jeans and stuffed them into a desk drawer. From his desk, he removed a carefully folded shirt, suit and tie. He was in the process of stepping into the pants when he happened to look up.

A woman was standing there.

It was not just any woman; she was clearly, from the Personnel memo in her hand and the shocked look on her face, his secretary.

'I'm Jean,' she said, haltingly.

She was a small, pert young woman who at this moment did not know whether to laugh or cry. Brantley did not know, either.

'Great,' he said. 'Uh — I'm not wearing anything.'

'I see that.'

'It was warm.' That's it, Brantley thought, take

78

command, be definite. 'Seems cooler now. I'll get dressed.'

This pleased Jean. 'Yes, sir. I'll move my stuff in.'

'Good idea.'

His new secretary gave him one more odd look. Then she closed the door to his inner office.

Good start, Brantley thought. It's always good to flash the new secretary on her first day. But he had no more time for self-recriminations. He just had to finish dressing.

When he was done, he cruised into the outer office. Jean jumped a bit when he entered, as if he might have more strange surprises for her. Instead, he laid a large bunch of papers on her desk.

They were the results of his labors: his conclusions about Pemrose.

'These are notes — charts, graphs, all kinds of things. They're arranged by different departments. Do your best. And order some poster boards, lots of colored pens, different colored pushpins, a T-square and drawing table, a compass, lots of pencils and my lunch. I'll be back.'

Jean started taking frenzied shorthand of all his demands. She was still writing, trying to keep up with him, when Brantley turned to go.

On his way out, he bumped right into a maintenance man. The burly older fellow carried a package.

'This where the nameplate goes?' he asked.

Brantley grinned. He nodded. Then he watched with undeniable pride as the man applied the plate to the front door.

'CARLTON WHITFIELD. 4319.'

Brantley couldn't have been prouder if it had been his own name.

CHAPTER TWELVE

Carlton Whitfield got used to his job.

And Pemrose Consolidated got used to Carlton Whitfield. It had yet to truly make his acquaintance, of course. But the other executives and lower employees got used to seeing Carlton. They saw him walking swiftly and aggressively down the halls. They saw him smiling brightly at the prettiest secretaries. They heard him chatting opinionatedly in the elevator. They passed his office and caught him reading *The Wall Street Journal*. They stood next to him in the executive washroom. They ate next to him in the cafeteria. They worked out next to him in the executive aerobics class.

And if they occasionally heard him whispering to himself as he walked — saying things like 'Okay, slow down. Walk arrogant. Look important' — well, all executives had their quirks. Anything that helped to make them powerful was okay with Pemrose.

Brantley Foster was getting used to Carlton Whitfield, too. While he still awoke with residual nervousness — and sometimes suffered from nightmares of being discovered — he had to admit it had gone fairly smoothly. He thought this one day as he sat casually amongst his colleagues in the Executive Lounge.

He looked across the room. He saw Christy Welles.

Brantley straightened his tie. This was his big chance, a tad different from barging into her office. He would talk to her, executive to executive now. He ambled nonchalantly over to her.

'Small world,' Brantley said, suavely.

Christy just looked blankly at him. 'Are you new in this department?'

Brantley tried not to blush *too* much. Okay, he thought, she's a busy woman, give her a break. She can't remember every fool who barges into her office. 'Brand new. Remember? Carlton Whitfield. And you're . . .'

It all came back to Christy. 'Busy.'

She moved immediately past him. She walked quickly over to another young executive.

'Brent, did you get those figures on transfer costs and insurance?' she asked him.

'Not yet,' he answered. 'Big delay in Chicago.'

'Damn,' Christy said. 'I need them now. You said you'd have them.'

The man shrugged 'Blame Chicago.'

Brantley saw another opportunity. If he could not impress her with his charm — or remind her of their good old days — then he would have to resort to flaunting his competence. He approached the two of them now.

'Maybe I can help,' he said.

'How?' Christy asked, sourly.

'Transfer costs and insurance for what?'

'By the time I explained, I could find it out myself.'

Forget the competence, Brantley thought. Bring back the charm. 'Explain at lunch. I'll have the answer before dessert.'

'I don't eat lunch.'

Brantley laughed, the sweat of failure watering his suit. 'Let's start again. Carlton Whitfield. And you're . . .'

'Annoyed.'

Christy moved quickly away from him again. She went to a nearby coffee machine. She began pouring herself a very agitated cup.

Brantley would not say die. Within a second, he was at her side again. He could not help feeling there was something else bothering her. How much could she wish to avoid *him*, anyway? He abandoned charm and competence and tried something entirely new: humanity.

'You know, I'm just trying to be friendly.'

This approach was effective. Christy dropped her harsh tone. She, too, sounded vaguely human now.

'You picked a bad time,' she said. 'I was counting on those figures.' She extended her hand. 'Christy Welles. How do you do.'

She did more than sound human now; she did something *very* human, uniquely human. She smiled at him.

Brantley held her hand warmly in his. He smiled back. He felt electricity coursing through their fingers up and down their bodies.

Then they were interrupted.

'Let's go!' someone called. 'Conference Room! Everybody!'

Brantley turned, distractedly. He noticed Prescott's most pewling assistant, Art Thomas, rounding everybody up. Christy turned to him and shrugged. Time for work, her smile said; her hand escaped from his. Brantley nodded, with the same corporate worldliness. He blindly followed her from the lounge.

Falling into a parade of young executives, they marched down the hall to the conference room. Brantley stayed attentively close to Christy, bringing up the rear.

'So, you don't eat lunch,' he said. 'Do you eat dinner?'

'Occasionally.'

'Tonight?'

'Booked.'

'Tomor —'

'Booked.'

'Anytime during this century?'

She looked at him with some of the old annoyance. Back off, Brantley told himself. This was one woman who does not like to be crowded, not even by someone as charming, competent and humane as Carlton Whitfield.

The line of executives entered the conference room.

83

The door closed behind Brantley.

He looked around. All of the young executives took their usual seats. All of them settled into yet another conference. Brantley looked behind him. He could not just bolt for the door. At the same time, where the hell was he supposed to sit?

Soon he was the only one left standing. Conspicuously, he shuffled uneasily. Art Thomas approached him then.

'Who are you?' Thomas snapped.

'Carlton Whitfield,' Brantley said, immediately. 'New employee.'

Thomas looked at him, suspiciously. 'I didn't get any memo on that.'

Brantley looked at the man's severe expression; he was so eager to keep order, so sure about his correctness. He was so easy to put down.

'You will,' Brantley said.

He smiled pleasantly at the annoyed Thomas. Then Brantley calmly took the nearest seat, one that placed him directly opposite Christy.

Thomas shrugged it off. Then he took his own place at the head of the table. He clearly had bigger problems on his mind. He let an expression of grave concern cover his face. Then he explained what the meeting was unfortunately all about.

'It's happened,' he declared. 'The worst has happened. A corporate raider, Donald Davenport, has filed a Thirteen-D.'

Murmurs of shock went all around the table. Brantley heard whispers of 'Thirteen-D . . . You're kidding . . . Oh, my God . . .' It was as if a case of plague had hit the company.

Brantley looked concernedly over at Christy. She was the only one who remained calm.

Trying to suppress his hysteria, Thomas continued. 'Davenport has acquired five percent of the stock as of this moment. This is definitely the beginning of a hostile takeover of our corporation.'

Brent, the man Christy had approached, now added his own fear and trembling. 'I think we all know what happened the last time Davenport took over a company. He stripped it clean — everybody was canned.'

Thomas gloomily nodded. 'From the Chief Executive Officer to the mailroom flunkies. Everybody.'

Brantley could not help but feel the crack about the mailroom was directed at him. He looked across again at Christy. She was as cool as ever. What did she know, he wondered, that everybody else didn't?

'The word has come down,' Thomas continued, 'from on high. Mr Prescott wants us to recommend cuts in every department. Our job is to slash the red ink because the corporation is going to need cash for its defense. Anybody want to fire the first shot?'

There was an uncomfortable pause. No one wished to be the first to volunteer wisdom. No one but Christy.

'Kill Toledo,' she said.

There was another patch of silence. Then her words hit home; everybody enthusiastically nodded and murmured agreement.

'If we close down our distribution centers in Toledo,' Christy expanded, 'and Joplin and Jacksonville, we'll slash the red ink completely off the books.'

There was more agreement expressed; everybody seemed to think Christy had the answer, the best way to save their necks.

Brantley, however, was not one of them.

Beautiful or not, Christy was off-base, he thought. His mind flicked back to his charts, graphs, deductions. He could not keep silent about it. He looked hesitantly around the table.

Then he raised his hand.

Thomas sighed. 'You don't have to raise your hand, Whitfield. Just — speak.'

'Well,' Brantley cleared his throat, abashedly, 'I know

I'm new here — and I know these cuts seem like a good idea on the surface.'

'Yes?' Thomas pressed. 'So?'

'But closing those distribution centers would really be a mistake.'

Eyes opened wider all around the table. More murmurs came from mouths, unhappy ones this time. Brantley did not even look at Christy; he could not. She, however, would not take this lying — or sitting — down.

'I'm confident that these closings are exactly what Mr Prescott wants,' she said, coldly.

'Then Mr Prescott hasn't thought things through very well, because closing these centers will plunge this corporation deeply into debt.' Brantley swallowed, with great discomfort. Was he being way too brash? He remembered a memo he had read that had said all this. He turned authoritatively to the man at his right. 'Ferguson here will back me up on that.'

'I'm Proctor,' the man said. '*He's* Ferguson.'

Brantley looked immediately to his left then. 'Well, tell them, Ferguson. You wrote a memo to Mr Thomas here explaining exactly what I'm saying.'

Ferguson looked at him, startled. 'That's true. But how do you know?'

'How?' Brantley thought quickly. 'That memo was a masterpiece! It was tacked to the bulletin board for three days before somebody stole it! Clear, concise and to the point — that was the best damn memo I ever read in my life.'

Ferguson smiled, flattered. 'Well, thank you.'

Christy cut in. 'Forget the memo. What's the point here?'

'We need to be bold,' Brantley said, slowly. 'We need to expand into the open market and take away the competition's customers.'

There, Brantley thought, now I've done it. I've alienated her forever. Still, there was something thrilling

about revealing details of his master plan for Pemrose —
in the middle of a corporate meeting, no less. He felt both
remorseful and extremely glad.

Christy just felt furious. She glared at Brantley as if she
wished him to self-destruct instantly.

'Christy,' Thomas said, awkwardly, 'this project has
been your idea from the start. What do you say to Mr . . .
uh . . .'

'Whitfield,' Brantley said.

Christy just kept staring cruelly at Brantley. There was
no chance she would suddenly praise him. 'Spunk' was
not going to be in Christy's reply.

She did not disappoint his expectations. 'It's reckless.
It's irresponsible. It's stupid.'

She looked down then, as if dismissing him forever. All
around her, executives erupted in conversation, pro and
con, on Brantley's side or Christy's. How has this turned
into me against her? Brantley wondered.

Thomas tried to keep order. 'All right — that's
enough! We'll pick this up again later.'

Thomas shook his head at the disruption. He shot an
accusing glance at Brantley, the disrupter. Then he
stormed out.

The arguing executives slowly followed him. Christy
left in the midst of them, her face red with rage.

He caught up with her in the corridor. He had to run to
reach her; he had to keep running to keep up.

'Do you ever plan to speak to me again?' he asked.

'Only in anger,' she replied.

Brantley wished to apologize for making her look
foolish. At the same time, he did not wish to take back
what he said; he still believed in it.

'Let me make it up to you,' he said, 'and buy you a
drink after work.'

'Not if my life depended on it.'

'You hate me?'

'You make it so easy.'

Christy threw him a chilled smile. Then she cut down a corridor, her cruel speed not inviting him to follow.

Brantley just watched her disappear. He felt dizzy from the meeting. He felt as if Carlton Whitfield had made his first big impression and his first big mistake. It had been quite a coming-out party.

He was late getting back to the mailroom. He flew in, his T-shirt still untucked, his left shoe untied.

Brady was waiting for him. He nearly rammed himself into Brantley's path.

'You — Harvard!' he said. 'Where have you been?'

Brantley may have been late but he was still prepared. He chucked Brady an envelope.

'Personnel,' he answered. 'You told me to wait for an answer. They're really slow up there, Chief.'

Brantley made to smugly retake his station. But Brady, though mixed-up, was not appeased.

'Something's going on here,' he said, quietly. 'I'm gonna be all over you like a rash from now on, Foster.'

'Won't the other guys get jealous?'

Brantley moved quickly to his place. As confident as he appeared, he feared that Brady's new surveillance could only cause him trouble. And Brantley/Carlton Foster/Whitfield was in enough trouble as it was.

CHAPTER THIRTEEN

Christy Welles felt her composure starting to crack.

Her composure was famous; it had gotten her through college, through business school and now it was getting her through the lowest echelons of Pemrose Consolidated.

But it almost didn't get her through the last meeting; she had almost lost it with that troublemaker Whitfield. And it might not get her through her dinner date tonight.

It was not really a date; it was a rendezvous, an assignation. It was just the kind of act she had promised herself to avoid, an action that could jeopardize the thing she cared most about on Earth: her career. Now she had fallen into two quicksands. Not only was her 'date' married, he was also her boss.

Howard Prescott.

She had fought him for as long as she could. Then a few weeks before, she had given in: to his power, to his appearance, to her own loneliness. What had she been thinking? She could not imagine.

She knew what she was thinking now: this was a big mistake. Still, the best she could do, the biggest protest she could make, was to be late for dinner. Cool, composed Christy Welles was helpless. The world was a poorly run company, she thought, chagrined.

Ahead of her, on the deck of the exclusive River Cafe in Brooklyn, she saw Howard sitting. He's pretty put out, she thought. Big rebellion.

'Where have you been?' he snapped. 'I've been waiting for twenty minutes.'

Christy put her briefcase down with a bang. Then she sat at their table. 'Don't start on me, Howard. It's been one hell of a tough day.'

Christy unsnapped the case and pulled out a typed sheet. She thrust it into Howard's hand. 'Here's the preliminary report. You'll need this tomorrow.'

Howard fingered the paper, grateful but dissatisfied. 'What I need tonight is a little understanding.'

'That's your wife's job, Howard. Not mine.'

Howard knew her no-no meant yes-yes. He reached across the table and took her hand. 'Look, Christy, this thing with Vera —'

'It's called marriage?'

'I'm still crazy about you and you know it. Those three weeks in August were the happiest in my life.'

Christy pulled her hand slowly from his grasp. 'Why are you telling me this? Is Vera planning another trip?'

Howard shook his head at Christy's cynicism. 'What we had was more than a fling. I would leave Vera now, tonight, but you don't just tear up a twenty-year contract until you work out all the details.'

Christy tried to shrug away his bull. She tried to divert herself — and retard the start of tears — with business. 'It was the consensus of the group that . . . '

'I need you, Christy.'

'Cutbacks in the Midwest region would supply the company with enough immediate cash . . . '

'You've got to stick with me. You're all I can really count on.'

' . . . to battle this takeover attempt. A dissenting opinion was offered by Carlton Whitfield, who . . . '

Howard shifted suddenly from romance to reality. 'Whitfield? Who's Whitfield?'

'A new Vice-President in Operations.'

'Who in the hell is hiring new employees?'

'Don't ask me. Ask Carlton Whitfield.' He'll tell you much *more* than you want to know, she thought, bitterly.

'Classic. This is classic!' A leader not a lover now, Howard broke a breadstick in frustration. 'This is Davenport's method all the way. He's a plant for Davenport. And if Davenport takes control of the company, we're both out of a job.'

Without tenderness, Howard looked into Christy's eyes.

'Get close to this guy and find out what he's up to.'

Christy took this like a shot in the mouth. First he tried to seduce her again; then he tried to seduce her in a different, more insidious way. Why couldn't she just get up and go?

'You're asking me to spy on him?'

Howard was all sweetness and light again. He took Christy's small hand into his own larger, more powerful one. 'You really have to do something about your vocabulary.' He smiled, silkily. 'I'm sorry, Christy. I know you hate this intra-office intrigue, but it's all part of the package, believe me. The company is in trouble and my head is on the block.'

She felt the tears again. 'I thought it was your wife who's supposed to relieve this kind of pressure.'

'You're tired,' he said, patronizingly. 'Let's get out of here. We'll go to your place and talk the whole thing over. I need you, Christy.'

Christy felt her hand go limp in his. The fight was over; he had won again; there was no rational reason.

First she would get in bed with Howard; then, in a manner of speaking, she would have to get in bed with Whitfield. Christy sighed. There were some things they did not teach you at Harvard Business School.

CHAPTER FOURTEEN

That night, Brantley had a date, too.

He wasn't dreading it, as Christy had been; he wasn't even expecting it. He came in late, after having done more shopping for supplies for his apartment. His arms full, he had not been able to turn on the light. Instead, moving cautiously, he had merely closed the door with a swing of his hip. Then he had given up trying to flick the light switch with his elbow.

Maneuvering in the dark, he had first kicked a chair halfway across the room. Then he had rammed a table with his knee. Then he had kicked a few things he could not identify. Only then had he put his packages down.

He felt his way back across the apartment, cursing his alley exposure. Finally, he reached a nightstand and pulled on a light.

Brantley screamed.

Lying in his bed, its cover hanging provocatively off her bare shoulder, was Vera Prescott.

'What are you doing here?!' Brantley cried.

'Howard's working late tonight,' she answered.

She was, of course, naked. She was also dreamy-eyed, flirtatious, and extremely attractive. Brantley made the mistake of sitting on the bed beside her.

Vera pulled him down to her. Brantley wiggled quickly away.

'No! You can't be in here! There are rules!'

Vera smiled, slightly. 'Don't be silly.'

'No, really,' he stammered. 'If the Super finds out, I'm

dead. How did you get in?'

'The Super let me in.'

Brantley sighed. New York apartment houses were not college dorms, he concluded. Neither were college dorms. He was speechless.

'Aren't you glad I came?' she asked, teasingly.

Brantley looked at her. He remembered their afternoon together on the divan in her back room. He remembered everything up until the moment Uncle Howard came home. He was forced to be honest.

'Sure. Yes. Sort of. I like you. But there are problems.'

'Such as?'

'Your husband is my boss!'

Vera shrugged. 'We won't tell him.'

'But we could get caught. Then he'd probably kill me and they'd ship my body back to Kansas, and I'm not ready to go back to Kansas yet.'

'Howard would never kill anyone. And were it not for Vera Pemrose, Howard would definitely not be sitting on top.' She eyed him, suggestively. 'Vera Pemrose can put *you* on top. Later.'

So Pemrose was her maiden name; she was the source of the bucks. Still . . . 'But you're my aunt,' he said.

'Oddly enough, that's part of the appeal. It makes me feel very — primitive.'

Without another word, Vera slid the sheet from her. She rose and stalked him. Brantley was paralyzed by the sight of her. Soon her arms were around him; the rest of her was pressed against him.

'You're not a little kid in Kansas any more, Brantley,' she said. 'Things are different here. Once you get used to them, things are better here, too . . . '

She kissed him then, a long, sensuous kiss. Brantley became putty in her hands. He let himself be kissed; he forgot everything else: Christy, Prescott, Pemrose, incest.

When she released him, he realized he agreed with her.

94

Kissing *was* better in New York.

Then there was a knock at the door. Brantley jumped.

'Christ!' Brantley whispered. 'I'm dead. I can't believe it.'

Vera sighed, shaking her head. Brantley slithered out of her arms and went to the door. He looked out of the peephole. He caught his breath.

'Uncle Howard!' he said, loudly. 'Jesus . . . what a surprise! Just a minute. The lock's jammed. Just a second.'

Brantley closed the peephole and looked, panicked, at Vera. She did not share his concern. She was only, calmly and quietly, dressing. He pointed feverishly at the back door.

'That leads to the street,' he whispered. Then he called through the door. 'Hold on, Uncle Howard! I'm getting the pliers! Just a second!' He whispered once more to Vera. 'He knows about us. He knows everything.' He was yelling again. 'Here they are! It won't be long now! Coming!' He looked, plaintively, at his aunt. 'What do I tell him? How do I explain all this?'

'For God's sake, Brantley,' she said, 'calm down. He didn't follow me. It's all a coincidence. Just pull yourself together.'

Brantley was rushing her out the back door to the boiler room. She gave him one last kiss and one last direct command.

'Be calm! He doesn't know.'

Then with a self-assured smile and her clothes back on, Vera was gone. Brantley gave a sigh of relief.

He opened the front door then. A messenger dressed all in black stood there, holding a Bible.

'Have you sinned, brother?' he asked.

'I certainly have,' Brantley replied.

'Then you need to talk to the Lord.'

Brantley smiled a little. 'Tell him to call my secretary and we'll have lunch.'

Brantley slammed the door in the man's face. He shook his head, with a weary smile. Let he who is without sin cast the first stone. He was sure his Uncle Howard had a few sins of his own.

CHAPTER FIFTEEN

Life became more difficult for Carlton Whitfield.

The next morning, Brantley arrived at work in a halfway state: dressed in T-shirt and jeans and carrying a briefcase. The effect was jarring, as if Superman had shown up in cape, tights and workshirt.

Melrose could not help but notice. He looked at Brantley's case with a jaundiced expression.

'What's in there?'

'My lunch,' Brantley said, quickly.

'In a *briefcase*?'

'I ran out of brown bags.'

Casually, Brantley tossed the briefcase into his mail bag. He started grabbing a large pile of incoming mail to take with him. He was trying to test doing a few things at one time.

Brady, however, had other ideas.

He blocked Brantley's path. Brantley sighed. It was like trying to move through a mountain.

'Wait, what's your hurry?' Brady asked, suspiciously. 'What's going on?'

'I've got a special delivery — marked urgent.'

Brady screwed up his face. 'I've got my eye on you, Foster. Every moment, God is watching.'

If that were the case, Brantley wondered, why did Barney Brady exist? With a polite smile, he hustled past his boss and out the door.

Once out of the mailroom, Brantley immediately stashed his mail cart in a service room. Then he quickly stepped into an open elevator.

The doors closed; the car began to rise. When it was a few floors up, going between floors, Brantley took a deep breath.

Then he pushed the 'Stop' button.

The car came to a jolting halt; Brantley nearly lost his balance. A bell blared out so loudly Brantley felt it must be heard all over town. Then he shrugged and did what he was there to do.

He fished his briefcase out of his mail bag. Then he quickly snapped it open. From it, he extracted his neatly folded suit and tie. He pulled his T-shirt over his head.

On Whitfield's floor, a small crowd had gathered around the elevator. Executives late for morning meetings stood, annoyed, looking at the dead car. They impatiently pushed the 'Up' button again and again.

'Is this thing dead, or what?' one asked.

They soon received their answer. The bell stopped sounding. They heard the car start to rumble. Then, within a matter of seconds, the door opened. That new executive, Carlton Whitfield, was in it.

He was straightening his tie, wiping sweat from his brow.

'Whew,' Whitfield said. 'Hair-raising experience. I'm all right now.'

Whitfield shook his head. Then he nodded at his colleagues and started off, quickly, to his office.

Brantley did not look back. He nearly ran into his office, hardly even stopping to address Jean.

He flipped her an audio cassette. The young woman caught it, instinctively, and then smiled, pleased with herself.

'Transcribe these notes,' Brantley told her. 'There are some things on there I need right away. Make me some copies of this, this, and this. Did you get those extra supplies? I need them right away. No calls. I'm busy all day. Be back later.'

And Brantley was gone again, out into the hall. He strode quickly back to the elevators, occasionally checking behind him for spies.

When he reached the cars, an elevator was waiting for him, as if he had called it. Smiling, he flew right in.

The car moved down this time. Before it could reach too many other floors, between two of them, Brantley hit the 'stop' button. The bell went off again. Brantley was nearly immune to it by now. He quickly began peeling off his suit, kicking out of his pants.

He did not know that a few floors above him, on the floor he had just left, there was some concern. Jean stood at the elevator, listening with annoyance to the blaring bell. An elderly janitor passed by; Jean got his attention. The old man tried pushing the button a few times, but to no avail.

'Damn this thing,' he muttered.

Jean sighed. Mr Whitfield was going to kill her if she didn't get this stuff done. She looked impatiently at the old janitor. Then he looked at her and winked. He knew just the thing.

Brantley was reaching for his mailroom clothes when the elevator jumped; he went flying onto the floor. He lay there, helpless, struggling to reach his pants, as the car flew back up. His eyes widened as he saw the digital charting of his journey. Not back to the forty-third floor.

'Oh, no!' he said, aloud. 'Jesus — oh, my God —'

Jean smiled her thanks to the old janitor. He walked away. The car was on its way back up. Then, in no time, the elevator had arrived. It stopped. The door opened.

Mr Whitfield was standing there in his underwear.

'Jean!' he cried. Then immediately, he became businesslike. 'Uh — I meant to tell you. Send my pants to the laundry for a quick press. See you later.'

Whitfield flung out his pants; Jean quickly caught

99

them. This time, she did not smile at her own coordination. She only stood and stared as her half-naked boss disappeared behind the closing doors.

CHAPTER SIXTEEN

The day was not over for Carlton Whitfield.

Sweating wildly, Brantley raced back to the mailroom. He immediately grabbed a pile of mail. He began throwing it hurriedly into slots, trying to look busy if not efficient.

Melrose was standing next to him. He watched as his friend fired off letters at high speeds into various boxes. He shook his head at how this kid operated. Melrose always took time to dawdle. Maybe this was the difference between them; maybe Foster was really going places and Melrose was staying in this place.

'What is it with you?' he asked. 'You're always in high gear.'

Brantley was out-of-breath. 'It's Brady. He's always watching me. I've got to keep moving.'

Melrose shrugged. 'You'd better watch yourself. I've seen guys working two jobs look better than you.'

Brantley just grinned, weakly. His letters, his hair, his feet kept flying.

On another floor, they were waiting for Whitfield. Around the long conference table, the executives sat, ready to go, anxious for the tardiest among them. A chair — now officially belonging to Whitfield — stood conspicuously empty across from Christy.

Art Thomas was peeved. He checked his watch. Then he figured, let the little troublemaker fend for himself.

'We can't wait for Whitfield any longer,' he said. 'Let's

get started. Sanderson has drawn up some projections that . . . '

The door burst open then. Carefully coiffed heads all turned in one direction.

It was Whitfield. Or part of Whitfield. The top half of him looked like an executive: shirt, jacket and tie. But the bottom half looked like — well, looked like a mail-room employee: jeans and sneakers.

The man seemed in some sort of fever. His face was red and wet. His eyes stared, wildly. He had a funny sort of half-mad smile on his face.

'Sorry — late — busy — hi,' he babbled.

Murmurs went around the table. Whitfield plunked himself down in the waiting chair. He just kept smiling, staring, panting.

'Casual attire today, Whitfield?' Thomas asked, archly.

Whitfield just looked at Thomas with the same crazy smile. Then he seemed to register the words.

'The jeans — right — a new product line. Thought I'd test them out.'

He looked, smiling, at his colleagues. His attention rested at last on Christy. She barely nodded hello. She looked a little disgusted with him. Then she just looked disgusted with herself and looked away.

Thomas cleared his throat. He wasn't about to let this showboat screw up his meeting. 'Now perhaps we can begin. Sanderson has drawn up some projections that I think we should all take a look at.'

Sanderson began to pass out some papers, seeming very pleased with himself. Brantley took up the sheets with relief. It would be nice for a change to worry about someone else's ideas. Maybe he could prove the fallacy of Sanderson's plan, too; *that* might be fun.

Then he noticed someone else was in the room.

Prescott stood in the doorway, trying not to be noticed. He was observing his employees, sort of springing a surprise quiz on them.

Brantley saw him from the corner of his startled eye. No one else seemed to have seen him. Maybe it was his imagination, Brantley thought. It *had* to be his imagination. Any other possibility might involve his own death.

But Prescott was no apparition. At the same moment, everyone else in the room caught sight of him. Quickly, slouchers sat up; gum chewers spit out; daydreamers woke up. Everyone turned their swivel chairs attentively to face their boss.

Brantley swiveled the other way.

'Mr Prescott!' Thomas cried, clearly stunned. 'What a surprise!'

Prescott smiled, thinly. 'Your report is a couple of days late, Art. Thought I'd stop in and see what the problem is.'

Thomas immediately smiled with deep discomfort. His was no match, however, for Brantley's discomfort. The new executive sat, scratching his eyebrow, lowering his head, keeping his face obscured.

'No real problems, Mr Prescott,' Thomas said, desperately. 'No, sir. We just have a few wrinkles to iron out that Whitfield has called to our attention.'

A knife went into Brantley's neck. Whitfield? Wrinkles? His mind shot miserably back to his mother in Kansas; he was crazily free associating. He wished he was back there this instant, driving a nice slow car for the druggist, selling feed, pumping gas. What was so great about making money, meeting beautiful women, becoming a success? Home, that's where the heart was. His heart was at home *and* stuck at the top of his throat.

Prescott nodded, with exaggerated interest. He shot a quick glance at Christy, which she studiously avoided. Then he began to walk farther into the room.

'I'll just join you for a few moments, if you don't mind.'

He did not sit near Thomas or Ferguson or Sanderson or Brent. He sat right next to Christy. He sat right across from Brantley.

103

His face bent halfway to the floor, Brantley could only make out parts of Prescott: his shoulder, his neck, the bottom of his chin. He was nearly faint from fear.

'Now,' Prescott said. 'Which one of you is Whitfield?'

There was a long pause. Every executive in the room turned to the man who was known by this name. Prescott began slowly turning in the same direction.

Brantley shot up.

He did not rise to identify himself, however. He rose with one arm whipped across his face, like Dracula about to strike.

'Nose bleed!' he shouted. 'Oh, my God! It's a bad one! Pardon me — terrible nose bleed. Get them all the time. Dry heat — it'll be okay. Pardon me.'

Brantley pushed past everyone. He dropped his arm — he could not see over his elbow to the door — and fluttered his tie up over his nose. He gave little cries of someone bleeding. Then he saw wood right in front of him. He felt his hand squeezing a doorknob. He saw paradise: a reception room. As he fled, he heard voices behind him.

'Who was that?' Prescott asked.

'Whitfield,' Thomas sighed.

He wasn't sure but, as the door closed behind him, he thought he heard someone getting out of a chair. Someone heavy. Someone old and powerful and suspicious. Someone a great deal like Howard Prescott.

Brantley was running from the reception room into the hall. He heard heavy, old, powerful and suspicious footsteps behind him.

He looked left and right. Then he opened the nearest door and went through it. He would just tell whoever's office it was that he had wanted the men's room. At least he knew it wouldn't be Christy.

It was a supply closet.

Brantley shut the door behind him. He stood in pitch black, accompanied only by paper, ribbons, typewriter cleaner and old typewriters. He heard the footsteps outside coming closer. He reached his hand over his head. He clutched the light cord and pulled.

Brantley screamed.

He was not alone. Before him were a male executive and a female secretary; they were so close together they were practically fused. Lipstick was all over the man's face. The woman at that moment had her teeth sunk into the man's ear.

'Oh!' Brantley said. 'Sorry. I need some supplies. I can come back later.'

The two did not even look up long enough to notice him. Brantley quickly pulled off the light again.

He opened the door. To his horror, Prescott was only a few feet away. He slammed the door shut again.

He pulled the light on. The woman was now licking the man's nose. Brantley smiled at them, very uneasily.

'On the other hand,' he shrugged, 'when you need supplies, you need supplies.'

Brantley began to gather up all kinds of things: pencils, pens, Liquid Paper, paper clips, thumb tacks.

'I'll take one of these and one of these . . . some of these . . . oh, these are good, lots of these . . . '

His arms full, he nodded his thanks to his accommodating hosts. They did not notice him one more time. Brantley pulled off the light.

He reentered the hall, with great trepidation. Weighed down by enough supplies to satisfy two executives, he looked this way and that. Prescott had obviously gone back to terrorizing his other employees.

He walked very slowly back to the elevator. Holding supplies he did not need, wearing pants that did not match his shirt, nearly unconscious from fatigue, Brantley thought a double life was not double the fun, merely double the trouble.

CHAPTER SEVENTEEN

Christy was not enjoying her new job, either.

The new position of spy was not an easy one to reconcile. Or to pull off. The first time she had to perform some 'duties' of her job, she found herself fighting off some serious self-disgust.

In addition to being a spy, she had to be a thief, as well. She lurked around Whitfield's office, ever eager to see him walk out. But his random entrances and exits — which she witnessed from around a nearby wall — were too frenetic for her ever to get a bead on him.

One night, she merely out-waited him. She waited for his secretary to leave, looking frazzled. Then it was another hour or more before she saw Whitfield — now dressed in T-shirts and jeans, probably for a racquetball match — leave, too. Then she made her move.

She walked into the darkened inner office. She scanned the cluttered desk of his secretary. Whitfield was working the poor woman to death, Christy thought; what a little slave driver.

This kind of hostility helped Christy deal with what she did next. She went through the secretary's drawers. She looked through envelopes, packages, file systems. She passed over paperback romance novels, changes of shoes and what seemed to be love letters. There was nothing confidential about Whitfield, only about Jean.

Checking that the outside door was shut, she moved next into Whitfield's place itself. She snapped on the light. She looked around, feeling deeply abashed. A person's office was in some ways as intimate as his home. God forbid anyone should go through *her* office in such a way.

Still, she could not stop herself. She heard Prescott's voice in her ears, giving her commands that she somehow had to obey. Someday, she thought, I am going to stop this whole thing.

She would have to start tomorrow, however. Tonight, she was too busy poking into Whitfield's papers, charts, figurings. Tonight she was too busy taking some of the more interesting examples of his work and bringing them to Howard Prescott.

It turned out to be quite a haul. How much of it would actually be revelatory, she did not know. Certainly she had seen no mention of Davenport's name anywhere. That was probably just Prescott's paranoia, she thought. She walked contemptuously into the older man's office.

Prescott looked up, surprised. Christy did not give him a moment for any endearments. She simply dropped the large envelope of Whitfield trivia on his desk.

'Here are some of the notes I found in Whitfield's office,' she said, coldly.

Prescott did not even bother with a Thank You. Immediately, he began tearing open the envelope, hungry for any incriminating information. Christy felt sickened watching him. He looked like a starving dog poring through a trash can.

'If you want anything more,' she said, 'you can go after it yourself.'

She shocked herself saying this. But she did not seem to have any effect on Prescott, who was still shuffling desperately through the materials. Finally, he looked up with an expression of frustration. He clearly had found no smoking gun. He looked at Christy, as if finally noticing she was there.

'You think he's working for Davenport?' he asked.

Christy laughed a little. Prescott asked her the way he

would an employee in a business conference, as if it might be fun to get an underling's point of view, as if you never knew where the next good idea was coming from.

She sneered a bit at him, as much as she could, she was still a novice at real rebellion. Then gathering up all her strength, she said the nearest to what she really wanted to say, which would have only taken two words.

'I have no idea. I'm out of the spy business.'

Not bad for a beginner, she thought. Then she turned around and walked out, not giving Prescott a chance to reply.

Perhaps she just had not wanted to hear his reply. From his expression, Christy sensed he did not take her little outburst seriously. Just women's excitability, he probably thought; she'll be back.

Not if I can help it, Christy thought.

She felt she needed a bath, some way to remove the stain of her subterfuge. That would take care of her. Then she had to somehow make it up to Carlton Whitfield.

CHAPTER EIGHTEEN

The next night, Brantley was back to being Brantley.

He was still in Carlton Whitfield's office, of course; he was still in Whitfield's clothes. But the work he was immersing himself in was pure Foster: an orderly disorder of graphs, charts, computer print-outs and projections. He was never satisfied with his figures, he was never sure that he was right. Despite the misery that his masquerade had become, he did not want to forget what its purpose was: to prove himself at Pemrose.

And he stayed late to find the proof. Like many other nights, he stayed long after the executives, even the cleaning women were gone. Only he and a few stray security people remained in the cavernous Pemrose building.

One woman was there, as well.

Christy had planned her ambush of Whitfield much as she had her surveillance of him. This time, however, she did not mean to mess him up. She could not quite bring herself to tell the truth — or even to desire his friendship — but merely to make amends. With that in mind, she stood, nervously, in the doorway of his office now.

Brantley did not look up to see her. He was too busy punching a calculator, carrying a one, finding the square root. Christy had to walk farther in to get his attention. He only looked up when he heard her heels.

'You're really dedicated,' she said.

Brantley jumped a little at the sounds. Christy herself felt her voice boomed in the silent building and blushed.

But Brantley's surprise soon turned to pleasure; he smiled, slowly. Christy's embarrassment soon turned to industriousness. She planned to apply herself to being humane just as she had to telling off Prescott.

'I've seen you working late,' she said, trying to appear casual, 'every night this week.'

'Well,' Brantley said, 'there's a lot to do. Besides, I'm new in town.'

'I'm old in town — but you know what I mean.'

Christy shook a little at her own informality. Looking at him, she realized they did speak the same language. They were both about the same age, both enormously ambitious, both attractive, both wary. The new intimacy made her more hesitant.

Brantley enjoyed it. But he, too, kept his distance. There was the danger of offending her again and the danger *she* might offend him. There was also — always — the danger of revealing his dual identities through some slip bred by trust.

Still, he could not deny that being alone with her was a real kick. And they were so alone, the only people in the place practically. The only people awake in New York, it seemed.

Christy began nosing around at all the papers before Brantley. She was not doing it for Prescott now, she was doing it for herself. What *did* this guy know? she wondered. Or what did he *think* he knew?

'So,' she said, 'what's all this supposed to be?'

'The heart and soul of an idea you thought was screwy,' Brantley said, protectively. 'Expansion in the Midwest zone.'

Christy nodded. She could not resist a smile — or a dig. 'I still think it's screwy.'

Brantley felt himself a little riled. She was starting already. 'Give the idea a chance, and maybe you'll understand it.'

'I've given the idea all the chance it deserves. I just

112

want to prove to you that my plan is right.'

It had just popped out of her mouth. Christy was shocked at herself again. Yet she did feel the need to justify herself to him, both to make up for her spying and merely to prove herself correct. Brantley was a pain but he was also a challenge.

Brantley sat up straight. The lines of business battle were drawn. Much as intellectuals duel with ideas and lovers with technique, these business people were about to fight with figures. It was all about money and — the two of them could sense somehow but would not say — it was all about something else, as well.

'Okay, lady,' Brantley said. 'This is one you can't win.'

'Can we get started right now?'

'That would be great!' Brantley said, delighted.

They started, each determined to convince the other. Christy made her own charts, diagrams, maps. She paced the room like a defense attorney, her beliefs her client's. As she moved, her hair shook a little loose from her combs; the slit in her skirt moved this way and that.

Brantley watched her, intoxicated. He loosened his own tie, removed his own jacket, as he threw in contradictions and embellishments. The atmosphere in the office grew heady; both were so fervent about what they believed, about what was so close to their hearts. The room was filled with passion, yet money was the only subject.

'How can you not understand?' Christy said at one point, frustrated. 'The elimination of salaries creates a war chest for the defense of the corporation. We can sell the facilities and equipment of those contribution centers and turn this crisis into a money maker. It slashes expenses and gives us liquid assets to fight the takeover, and allows us to stop Davenport.'

Brantley was now way beyond being diplomatic. He put on a scoffing expression. 'You're too stubborn to admit that you're wrong. You won't stop Davenport that way. Closing those centers will panic the market. The shareholders will know the company's desperate. They'll run to Davenport and beg him to buy their shares.'

Christy shrugged. 'So we'll outbid him. We'll have enough assets to —'

Brantley thought she was beautiful when she was naive. 'No, you won't. Because if you close those centers, you put thousands of people out of work. You waste all your efforts on severance pay, unemployment contributions, union law suits and company guarantees on pension funds.'

This stopped Christy for a minute. She looked at Brantley, half-admiringly, half-infuriatedly. Brantley only beamed. Here he was, actually *being* an executive, whatever his name, actually getting his points across. And Christy, unlike Prescott, was actually listening.

Both suddenly sensed dangerous territory. Christy pulled back and walked in the opposite direction. Admitting Whitfield may be right felt weird; it almost felt arousing. She was a little sorry she had stopped by; still, something told her she wouldn't have missed it for the world.

Brantley felt endangered, as well. If he felt *this* close to Christy, how would he ever tell her the truth of who he was? Would she still listen to a mailroom boy's ideas?

Both suddenly looked at the other. Then both had the same idea at the same time.

They would continue this over a drink.

CHAPTER NINETEEN

The Empire Diner was open late. It was a popular Art Deco restaurant in the Chelsea neighborhood, on the West Side in the twenties. It looked like a side-of-the-road diner from the nineteen thirties; the clientele was young and affluent.

Brantley and Christy fit right in, with their appealing features and their well-tailored clothes. But they were oblivious to their surroundings or how well they suited it. Both hardly looked down at their spaghetti and Vodkas; both just shuffled substances in their mouth in order to get the energy to go on arguing.

'So,' Christy said, 'what's *your* great solution for this crisis?'

It was so simple to Brantley. 'We don't cut anything. We expand.'

'What!' Christy was incredulous. 'Expand where?'

'The Midwest zone. We can turn it into the biggest money maker in the company simply by eliminating one problem — transportation.'

Christy was blank-faced. 'I don't get the point.'

'Two things,' Brantley explained. 'First we need to buy a couple of trucking companies. Second, we need to build two more . . .'

'Build! Now you *are* crazy. We're set for a hostile takeover and you want to build?'

The idea was too audacious for Christy; that made it both frightening and exciting. The adjectives suddenly seemed appropriate for Brantley, as well. In his small frame, behind his all-American demeanor, was someone who obviously wished to test himself and others.

Christy knew that was part of what attracted her to Prescott — besides some obvious father thing she did not care to think about. Howard's brazen, robber baron style, his larger-than-life personality — they gave her a charge. She, too, wished to be that way; she knew that something always held her back. Now she had the same feelings about Whitfield. The differences were: Whitfield wasn't married, Whitfield was her own age, Whitfield seemed like he might actually be kind. She was tired of men who lied. Whitfield looked too innocent for any intrigues.

Brantley could tell he was getting across to Christy. Behind her take-charge front, he sensed this was a woman who feared true risk. There was something sweet about that; she might put the reins on him, provide some perspective, a sense of reality. Even now, she was watching him eat with a gentle, nearly maternal concern.

'That's not the way to eat spaghetti,' she said. 'You should twirl it around your fork.'

Brantley was just stabbing the pasta with his utensil. As many strands as he could impale, these he would then stuff into his mouth. He smiled, condescendingly, at her correction.

'Wrong,' he said. 'A common mistake made by pasta eaters who don't know beans about pasta.'

Christy became indignant. 'My grandmother was Italian. I know a little something about pasta.'

'Then you should know that pasta absorbs like a sponge. It draws the sauce into it and if you chop it, you release the flavor into the open air, instead of stifling it.'

Christy laughed out loud. This guy thought he was expert on everything, from stocks and bonds to spaghetti and meat balls. Who died and left him God? Correcting him was a pleasure; she could never do anything like it with Howard.

116

'That's ridiculous,' she said. 'And why do you put so much parmesan cheese on it? That's like taking a fantastic steak and smothering it with ketchup.'

Bits of pasta dangled out of Brantley's mouth as he self-assuredly explained. 'No — on steak, you put honey. A thin coat. Then you spread a little sour cream and hot peppers on it, and top it off with butter and mushrooms. After that, you smother it with ketchup.' Brantley turned. 'Waiter, could I have some more cheese, please?'

He grinned then, pleased with himself. Christy shook her head. He wasn't the only one who was pleased with him.

Once they finished eating, they did not leave each other. Without speaking, both expressed the desire to remain. At three in the morning, they could have gone to a dance club — but then they couldn't have heard themselves speak. So they decided just to wander.

They ended up downtown, in Soho, in the heart of the artists' district. Everything was closed; the large converted warehouses looked down on them like people in power. They felt dwarfed; they also felt invincible; they were the only ones up, after all. They had the means to work through the night and take over.

Brantley and Christy stood in front of Noguchi Sculpture, a chic gallery. They looked in through the darkened windows, making out strange shapes and forms, molding them in their minds to their own liking. It was like trying to make out what they were beginning to mean to each other.

Christy watched him watching the works. Then she suddenly decided to give him a break, to join him a little. Without warning, she reached into her briefcase and brought out an envelope. She tapped him on the shoulder. She placed it in his hand.

'What's this?' Brantley said.

'It'll only give you a glimmer of hope,' she allowed. 'Your plan still isn't going to work, so why get into it?'

117

She was being coquettish; the envelope was like a brief, dry, frustrating flirtatious kiss.

'Come on,' Brantley said, intrigued. 'Tell me.'

'All right.' Christy went further now. 'I did some checking and found out we *can* get some tax breaks from the Midwest states if we put up a facility in the region.'

Brantley was stunned. Why hadn't she told him this before? It was as if she had been playing hard to get; now she was turning off the lights herself.

'You got any other ideas like that?' he asked.

'A couple,' she teased. 'But I'm telling you . . .'

'Yeah, I know — it won't work. Tell me anyway, okay?'

Christy paused, teasing him more. It would mean getting involved, going all the way. How had she let it go this far?

Christy let out a long breath. Why not? What had she been waiting for? As another woman might give her body, she began to give her — conciliatory, agreeable, complementary — ideas.

CHAPTER TWENTY

The night continued.

Christy's succumbing lent the evening a new calmness now. They no longer argued; they just strolled with a pleasant feeling of financial afterglow.

They found themselves on the Lower East Side now. They stared into windows displaying incredible sales; they looked, entranced, as if viewing displays of their own business acumen.

Christy yawned yet she felt truly awake. She felt as if she had only now awoken to herself. And to Whitfield.

'So how come,' Brantley wondered, 'you're always so mad at me?'

Christy shrugged. 'I don't know. I've been mad since I met you.'

'A lot of people are like that,' Brantley smiled. 'The next thing you know, they get married.'

Christy just shrugged him off; don't spoil the mood, pal, she thought. 'Don't hold your breath.'

But Brantley was persistent, never one to take no for an answer. Would she question his 'experience'? He smiled at the prospect, thinking of Vera Prescott.

'No, I mean it,' he said. 'I think you're secretly crazy about me, and you'd feel a lot better if you'd just admit it.'

He was cajoling her now, there on the empty street. Figures and finance were suddenly absent from his consideration. Now it was just the two of them, beneath their suits, down to *real* business.

'Come on,' he said. 'Give me a chance. I'm sort of an acquired taste.'

They continued downtown, as if the more honest they became, the farther they would descend, until they reached the core of themselves. They saw the glimmers of the South Street Seaport ahead of them. They saw the dawn, too; they had been walking that long.

Brantley went beyond the present now; he felt compelled to share the past with her. How else could he ever begin to tell her the truth?

He took out his wallet. He removed the second half of his round-trip ticket back to Kansas.

'My Dad insisted on buying me this round-trip bus ticket,' he said. 'I almost turned it in for a refund a couple of times, but now it's become a sort of symbol. The day I use this ticket is the day New York has beaten me.'

Christy saw something else in him then: a small boy straight out of the sticks, looking for acceptance. She was looking for that, too, all the time. Brantley met her eyes. He saw their similarity, too.

'I just noticed,' he said. 'You're sort of a mess.'

'Thank you,' she smiled.

'Anybody ever told you that before?'

'You're the first.'

'So how can you look so incredibly beautiful when you're such a mess?'

This was it: the moment to act or to cut and run. The moment when all the symbolism of their business talk would be forgotten. There would be no more innuendo, only ardor; no more substitutes, just the real sensation. They had a choice to make. They made it.

They shied away.

Brantley and Christy walked slowly through the Seaport, past the few lovers and the few homeless people who were still there. They veered slowly back towards business, the way divers shy away from the high board after a frightening fall. Yet the experience had happened;

120

they would not forget the leap.

'When two people work together on a project,' Christy explained, 'there's a danger of becoming emotionally involved.'

'That would be bad?' Brantley asked.

'Well, they confuse the intensity of their involvement on the project, and mistake it as an involvement with each other.'

Brantley laughed. 'What are you, a shrink?'

Christy, however, remained serious. 'It happened to me once. It's sort of still happening, I guess. And then the project ends and they find they don't have anything to talk about any more.'

'Then it's agreed.' Brantley said, still jaunty. 'We won't fall in love while we're working on this project.'

'Right.'

It *seemed* right. What had he asked her to promise? Christy couldn't even think. The liquor and the talk and the early hour were getting to her. She only knew that she was afraid, suddenly. Afraid of what she would do, afraid of what she would feel. She couldn't help it, she was also afraid of Prescott finding out. She was still afraid of him, maybe of losing him.

Brantley was faintly amused. Christy was fighting it so obviously, so hopelessly. Still, he could not help but feel concerned by her concern. Something was clearly bugging her. Or someone.

They ended up on the Staten Island Ferry. It did not make any sense; they did not care. They found themselves sailing into the sunrise; it felt like being in an old movie and not on a means of mass transit.

The warm wind fiddled around their faces. Brantley felt a little giddy; what an unexpected evening it had been. He felt determined to get Christy out of her funk.

'So,' he said. 'Who is he?'

'Who?'

'My competition.'

'Just a guy.'

Come on, Christy, he thought, you can do better than that. 'Let's call him up right now and tell him you've found a new guy and the whole thing is off.'

'I can't call him. Ever. His wife might answer the phone.'

Brantley stopped. He saw the real pain on Christy's face; he heard and re-heard her confession. He was surprised at her, nearly disapproving. How could she be so foolish? Didn't she know she would just get hurt?

Then he thought of himself, of Vera Prescott. It had all seemed so innocent, *was* so innocent in its way. Yet he saw now in Christy how treacherous such involvements could be. It was different when it went beyond some skinnydipping and divan-hopping. He wanted to protect her from more pain.

'Big mistake,' he said.

His solicitous tone annoyed her. 'Let's not talk about it any more.'

'I've done a lot of stupid things . . .'

'I bet you have.'

'But I never . . .'

'Ever?'

'— *never* have been involved with a married man.'

Christy laughed then; so did Brantley. She saw how he was not judging her, just trying to kid her out of her mood. He seemed to understand; this surprised her.

'He was sort of separated when we started,' Christy said.

'He says.'

'Yeah, well, that turned out to be a lie . . .' Christy thought then it wasn't just any married amn they were describing. It was Whitfield's boss, the man around whom their 'project,' all their plans, revolved. Christy suddenly felt deeply insincere, as if still playing both sides of the fence, still spying on Whitfield. She wanted to tell him the truth but she could not. 'All right, so the whole

122

thing was a mistake. We live, we learn, we move on, we
—'

Kiss, Brantley thought. It was what he did then; wrapped his arms around her and pulled her close and kissed her.

Suddenly, it did not matter what indiscretions they had committed or were still committing elsewhere. It did not matter what the risks of their involvement were.

They parted, each panting a little.

'That wasn't bad,' Christy said.

'Thank you.'

'Can you do it again just as good?'

Brantley smiled. He was always one to apply himself.

With Christy, Brantley's little apartment seemed like a penthouse suite. With Christy, his bed felt twice as big, his ceiling twice as high. The music from his radio sounded as grand as the Philharmonic; Doritos and beer tasted like a catered feast.

This time, all the happy noise was coming from *his* place. Brantley looked across at his wall and smiled at his unseen, insatiable neighbors.

Eat your heart out, he thought.

CHAPTER TWENTY-ONE

It was a very long evening.

As far as Christy was concerned, it could have gone on forever. With Whitfield, she did not even think of problems. They hardly even discussed business after a while. She even felt comfortable calling him Carlton.

The whole thing gave her new confidence. Why was she punishing herself staying involved with Howard? Why wasn't she acting as a free, young, ambitious woman should? Why had it taken her so long to find someone like Carlton?

Christy prepared herself as she approached the Pemrose building Monday morning. She was not going to declare herself through with spying; she was going to declare herself through with Howard.

When she reached the front of the Pemrose headquarters, she saw someone she was not prepared to see.

Howard Prescott himself.

Christy took a deep breath. She knew it was put up or shut up time; she just hadn't expected the time to come so soon.

Howard fulfilled all her expectations. He looked at her as if she had a lot of explaining to do, as if she had deeply disappointed him. He also looked beside himself with jealousy — or as close as he could come — and this pleased Christy.

'Where were you all night?' he nearly shouted.

Howard was on the ropes already; this gave Christy courage. She was going to enjoy twisting him around her finger, as he had twisted her around his.

'You could at least start with good morning,' she said, coolly.

Then she walked right past him into the building.

All day long, he would not leave her alone. Christy got so she could recognize Prescott's telephone ring. It seemed to be short and piercing, like a man spitting out expletives. She let it blow off some steam before she answered. And when she did, she did innocently, as if she could not imagine who in the world would be calling.

'Yes?' she said.

'I'm madder than hell,' Prescott said.

Christy paused, as if she were taking a minute to figure out who it was. Then she sighed, audibly, to show annoyance and replied with impatience.

'Oh. Hello, Howard.'

'I'm madder than hell,' he repeated.

Christy just murmured 'Uh huh'; she had heard this already.

'I want to know why you weren't answering your phone,' he went on.

Because I was making love with Whitfield, Christy thought. Again and again and again. Still, she could not quite say that. So she spoke as if Howard knew the score, as if it had only been a matter of time.

'I owe a lot to you, Howard,' she said. 'I'll always be grateful to you for the chance you gave me in this company and the things I've learned.'

There was a long pause. Gotcha, Christy thought; Howard was apparently dumbfounded. Finally, he reacted with the bafflement of a teenage boy being dumped.

'What is this?' he asked. 'What are you leading to?'

Christy gave a small snort of a laugh, as if she did not want to belabor the obvious. 'I want to work with you. I respect you more than you know. I appreciate everything. But I can't be involved with you outside the office anymore.'

There, Christy thought, I've said it. The words I've been waiting weeks to say. She looked out the window near her desk. Funny, no thunder clouds were forming, no lightning was striking; the world went on as it was going. Funny about that.

There was a long pause. Then Howard did what she had feared — or maybe even hoped — he would do.

He hung up.

Christy looked at the dead receiver in her hand. She could not help smiling a little; at the same time, she felt afraid. Risk was fun *and* frightening, she thought.

Christy hung up the phone. She shrugged to herself, feeling her fear start to subside. Then the door to her office sprang open.

Howard walked in.

He closed the door behind him. He was trying to seem calm, trying to be cool. But his face was a strange shade of red and his smile was enormously strained.

'Look,' he said, very fairly, 'I'm not going to pressure you on this. I want you to just take your time and decide what's best for you.'

The least he could have done was knocked, Christy thought.

'Thank you,' she sneered.

Then Howard chuckled, as if life was just so strange, wasn't it? He waited for Christy to inquire as to his mirth, but she did not. So he had no choice but to share his amusement unrequested.

'The timing is a little ironic, though,' he said. 'I was going to tell you last night that Vera and I have agreed on terms for a divorce.'

There was a long pause. Christy felt a slight queasiness in her stomach, a chill fall down her back. She tried to remain strong, tried to keep her determination. Yet Prescott had pushed the right button. She felt herself slowly begin to weaken.

127

Was it true? she wondered. Had it ever been? Suddenly, she did not care what their history had been; today, in her office, Howard seemed desperate enough to be telling the truth. At least that was the truth she wished to believe.

Christy could not respond for a minute, so confused was she. Howard took the lead.

'We've already made plans to meet with our attorneys to finalize the agreement.'

Christy was more than weakening now; she was well on her way to being completely helpless. All at once, Whitfield seemed a desperate encounter, a way only to forget what she felt for Howard. She saw herself as Mrs Prescott, powerful, protected and where she wished to be. What could Whitfield offer that could in any way compare?

'Howard, I . . . ' she whispered. 'I feel so badly.'

He had her back; he had her more strongly than before. And Prescott knew it. He turned the knife just a little deeper.

'I only wish Vera and I could have worked things out sooner. Maybe then there could have been some hope for you and me . . . '

He looked off, wistfully, as if musing on what might have been. Christy couldn't help it, she looked off with him. Tears came to her eyes. He looked at her, compassionately, as if he knew tears were hard to resist.

Prescott reached out and took Christy's limp hand. He held it, nearly held it up. Then from his inside jacket pocket, he took a letter and placed it between her fingers.

'This arrived this morning by messenger,' he said. 'Davenport has requested a meeting with the Board of Directors on Monday. He's offered to take over the company for thirty dollars a share in cash. I've called an emergency meeting and I'm asking all key personnel to spend the weekend at my house in Litchfield. And I would like you to be there, too.'

Christy thought it over, her head all cloudy. It seemed only right that she share this moment — one they had both been awaiting and dreading — with Howard. Besides, she could not help but feel flattered that she was included in 'key personnel.'

'Of course I'll be there,' she said, proudly.

Prescott smiled, warmly, so touched at her loyalty. Then he moved even closer and took Christy's other hand into his. He held her now; she could not have run away if she wished.

'One other question,' he said. 'Personal?'

Christy pulled back a little, but not too far; she was his. 'What, Howard?'

'Just out of curiosity — who were you with?'

The question, which she had been fearing, did not seem so horrible. Whitfield was, after all, a fling, a rebound; Prescott would understand. Besides she felt the need to confess and be forgiven by him. She sensed she would have told him if he had not asked.

'Whitfield,' she said. 'But it was . . . all business. We worked the whole weekend. Some of his ideas are brilliant.'

She had chickened out, she realized. Something in her could not part with Whitfield, with the memory of what they had shared. Something in her could not reconcile sacrificing him to Prescott; such an admission would have been a sacrifice, she had no doubts.

Howard gave a strange smile. 'I'm looking forward to hearing his ideas. I'll talk to him today.'

What strange inflections Howard gave to those words, Christy thought. He made 'hearing' and 'talk' sound positively violent. Her instinct to protect Whitfield grew stronger.

'One other thing,' she said. 'I'd like to have Whitfield's notes back. The ones I took from his office.'

Prescott paused, suspiciously. Then he seemed to scoff at himself. 'Of course. I'll get them to you.'

Christy sighed at Prescott's underhandedness and at her own reaction. What a mess they both had made!

'If you'd only been honest, Howard,' she said.

'I made a mistake, Christy,' he admitted. 'That's how much I wanted you.'

He squeezed her hands one final time. Then he left her. She looked after him, longingly, Carlton Whitfield far from her mind.

CHAPTER TWENTY-TWO

Christy was on Brantley's mind. She and nothing else were obsessing him that morning; thoughts of Pemrose and power were far away.

As he sat in Whitfield's office, adjusting his suit and tie, he thought all of their problems could be solved. Christy was sure to break off this thing with a married man; how could she not after their long weekend? As for the Whitfield masquerade, well, he was sure she could understand. She might have done some peculiar things for *her* career along the way, too.

Together, working on their plan for the Midwest region, he and Christy would be an unbeatable team. Like Paine and Webber, Smith and Wesson.

Prescott might have to look to his laurels with such a team on his tail. Brantley began imagining how his office would be when it was really his. No more hiding, no more lying, no more pretending. No more Brady.

It was with this confidence that he strode out, Whitfield disguise in place, into the hall. He walked as if he had never heard of the mailroom. He had a smile for the left of him, a smile for the right of him.

Furthest right, walking away, he saw Christy.

She was walking slowly, as if burdened by thought. Probably has me on her mind, Brantley thought, cockily. He picked up his pace in her direction. Then he sidled up right beside her. He gave her his best seductive look.

'Excuse me, Miss,' he said. 'I'm a reporter for the *New*

York Times. You look like a woman who has recently been made love to.'

To his surprise, Christy was having none of it. She looked unpleasantly surprised to see him. Her lack of speed had indeed been from unpleasant consideration.

'Not here,' she said.

Brantley understood: she was worried about her reputation. Brantley understood because he had two reputations to worry about. He continued being playful; she was fun to tease when she was so solemn.

'Oh, you weren't made love to here? Well, was it anywhere within the state lines of New York? We let the *Philadelphia Gazette* cover Philadelphia and New Jersey.'

Christy was doing something worse than not laughing; she seemed about to cry.

He stopped his clowning. He lowered his voice to a perturbed whisper. 'You all right? You look upset.'

Christy *was* upset, and Whitfield was only making it worse. Having him there brought home the full jolt of how she had behaved with Prescott. How could she have forgotten about Whitfield so easily? Was she *that* needy? She looked at him, unable to explain but unable to mask how confused she felt.

'I hate men,' was all she said.

'Well, I'm glad I'm not one,' Brantley replied.

Again, more tears than laughter. Brantley took Christy quietly aside. He hated seeing her so upset; he could only surmise it was the 'other man' situation that was upsetting her. He had a terrible need to be better than this bozo, to be someone who solved her problems, not caused them.

He had a terrible desire to tell her the truth about himself.

He did not know what reaction he would get. He only knew that, if it came out later, from anyone but him, it would hurt twice as bad. Better she should hear it now; then they would be truly together.

132

'There's something I've got to explain to you,' he said.

'You're not married, are you?' Christy said, with black humor.

'No. But there's something I have to clear up.'

This was all too much for Christy. She nearly crumbled; her bottom lip trembled. How many more scenes could she take today?

'We'll have a true confessions party,' she said. 'I have something to tell you, too. I did something I wish I hadn't done, and . . . ' It seemed impossible to tell him. He was so sweet; what he had done could only be dwarfed by *her* indiscretions. 'We'll talk about it.'

'How about this weekend?'

He *had* to bring up this weekend. Christy felt even worse. She immediately tried to end the conversation; Brantley was looking at her in that corn-fed, innocent way of his. She had to escape that look and what she felt for it.

'Can't,' she said, evasively. 'Some loose ends I have to tie up.'

She did not know if she meant to end it with Howard or to run away with Howard that weekend. She could not explain anything else to Whitfield.

Suddenly, she saw that he wasn't even paying attention. Whitfield was looking over her shoulder at the elevator. His eyes were widening with great amazement.

Brantley had seen Brady.

The mailroom boss had just come out of the elevator. This was unprecedented; Brady rarely left his basement lair, like a rat hiding beneath a house. Whatever the occasion was, Brantley did not want to know. He only wanted to get out of there.

Brady turned, He looked in Brantley's direction. Then he squinted, as if indeed a rodent adjusting his sight to the light. He saw someone he knew, someone he hated, someone who shouldn't have been where he was.

College Puke.

Brantley immediately turned to Christy, a fast sweat breaking out on his brow.

'Something's just come up,' he said.

'I've gotta run.'

Brantley ran. He took off around the corner, leaving Christy mystified. He did not look behind him, but he could hear Brady begin his pursuit. It wasn't hard; it was like hearing an elephant dance.

Christy turned. She saw coming towards her that fat, unpleasant man with whom she occasionally dealt in the mailroom. He wasn't coming to have a pleasant chat with her; he seemed bent on catching Brantley.

Brady nearly knocked into Christy. He took time for a quick courtesy.

''Scuse me,' he panted. 'Pardon me.'

Then he disappeared around the same corner. Christy wondered why a mailroom man would be chasing an executive. Then she merely shrugged and walked away, lost in her own considerable troubles.

Brantley would have loved to have been lost. Instead he was running in full view down a barren hall. He stopped when he reached the door marked 'Stairwell.' As he heard the fat feet of Brady coming his way, he immediately pulled open the door.

One stair at a time wasn't good enough now; neither were two stairs. Brantley jumped three stairs at a time until he was down another floor. Then he heard the 'Stairwell' door swing open. He heard Brady's legs carrying him as fast as he could down the stairs. One at a time.

Brantley pulled open the door at the next floor. He swung it carefully closed behind him. Then he did not slow his pace as he headed into a much more crowded hallway.

He nearly clipped several executives as he came coursing around a corner. He heard confused whispers of 'Wasn't that Whitfield?'

He was pleased with the recognition, displeased with

the attention. Then he almost barreled into another man and quickly put on his brakes.

It was a fellow picking up mail from a basket at a mail drop. It was a fellow dumping the mail with carefully studied indifference into his cart.

It was Melrose.

Melrose, of course, was wearing his usual uniform of an apron over T-shirt and jeans. Brantley, as he came to a halt, realized he was still in his suit.

Melrose just stared at him a minute. Brantley leaned casually against the basket, as casually as a man can who can hardly breathe. He smiled uncomfortably at Melrose. Melrose only furrowed his brow.

'What — Brantley?'

Brantley had no time to explain. He could only trust in his friend's friendship — or his discretion.

'You didn't see me,' he said. 'I wasn't here.'

Brantley blew off then, like the Road Runner in a cartoon. Within seconds of his disappearance, Melrose had the misfortune of greeting another visitor.

Brady came wheezing around the corner. When he saw Melrose, he came to his own sudden stop.

'Where'd he go?' he bellowed. 'Where is he?'

'I didn't see him,' Melrose chanted. 'He wasn't here.'

Brady turned. Brantley *was* there — or almost there. The young mailroom worker was busy maneuvering his way around several painters who were coating the corridor wall. After he had with agility danced around their cans and ladders, he flew into an 'Up' elevator.

Brady shot Melrose a dangerous look. Melrose merely shrugged, innocently. Then Brady had no time to lose; he headed for the stairs to head Brantley off at the pass.

The 'pass' turned out to be the floor from which they had both come: Whitfield's floor, Christy's floor. The floor on which Christy was still walking, contemplating her next move.

Brantley's next move was to come out of the elevator

there. He ran back towards the safety of Whitfield's office. On his way, he passed Christy again.

He had no time for a chat.

'Still here?' he said, speeding by her. 'You look great. Gotta go.'

He was heading away from her when he saw Brady emerging from the stairwell door, like the Creature from the Black Lagoon. He immediately turned and ran the other way, passing Christy once more.

Christy only watched, mesmerized, baffled, as Whitfield went down another stairwell. She watched, too, as that fat man — after a suitable period for catching his breath — went after him.

By this time, Melrose was leaning against the wall, just waiting for the racers again. He checked his watch; should be any minute now.

It *was* any minute. Brantley came running by, his face now completely empty of color. He only managed a pooped nod at Melrose.

'At the end of the second lap,' Melrose told him, pleasantly. 'You've still got a comfortable lead.'

Brantley smiled his thanks. Then he went into his dance again: he deftly avoided collision with the painters and their paints. After that, it was into another elevator.

Melrose waited a few more seconds. Then Brady came waddling by, *his* complexion somewhere between green and gray. He did not even have the energy to threaten Melrose.

Melrose thought the race had been fair long enough. He thought Brantley — just for being a very strange guy — deserved some kind of advantage. He had a good idea.

He stuck out his leg and tripped Brady.

Brady didn't know what hit him; he only knew something had. His big body went flying forward, sailing headfirst onto a secretary's desk. But he didn't stop there: his topspin was too great. Dragging all the desk supplies with him, he sailed like a launched whale into the group of painters.

Before he took off down the stairs, Melrose saw the head of the mailroom aimed straight for a can of Off-White.

Brantley owes me one, he thought.

CHAPTER TWENTY-THREE

Brantley made it to someplace safe: an office he was pretending to occupy.

He quickly closed Whitfield's outer door behind him. He could barely stand; he felt his knees beginning to buckle. He looked up, in order to provide Jean with some suitable far-fetched explanation — which he had yet to formulate — and breathed a bit easier. His secretary wasn't there.

Howard Prescott was.

Brantley forced a terrified smile upon his sweating face. For a minute, he wondered who he was: Whitfield? Foster? So did his boss.

'Brantley?' he asked.

Brantley just stood there, frozen. He hadn't had time to recover from his chase; now he was into another intrigue. He opened his mouth but no words came. Finally, he settled on a pleasant, baffled, goofy grin.

'What are you doing here?' Prescott wondered.

'Uh . . . ' Brantley thought. For a second, he could come up with nothing. Then he chose the most obvious — and plausible — idea. 'Looking for Whitfield. Special delivery for him.'

That was easy, Brantley thought. And not bad thinking, if he had to say so himself. Then Prescott erased his relief entirely.

'Why are you wearing a suit?'

This question was harder — and had, of course, no sensible answer. Brantley could only come up with the most far-fetched and yet unassailable possibility.

'This suit? Because of, uh, the funeral.'

There was a pause. Brantley immediately took on a mournful demeanor. He dropped his head and kicked an imaginary rock, with regret. Who would challenge that? Only a philistine, only someone deeply insensitive.

Only Howard Prescott.

'Whose funeral?'

Whose funeral? None of your business, Brantley thought. Where were you brought up, in a barn? Still, the boss was the boss and his stupid questions had to be respected.

'A friend,' Brantley said. 'He died. They buried him.'

Prescott didn't buy this but he had no interest — or time to lose — in disputing. He decided instead to dismiss Whitfield, his annoying loss and his aggravating grief.

'Where's Whitfield?' he asked.

Brantley looked around, just as confused as Prescott. He could have sworn . . .

'He isn't here?' he echoed.

This further piqued Prescott. He rolled his eyes, as if cursing his own lineage. Then he did something that made Brantley — who was already dripping with the stuff — sweat more.

Prescott touched his paperwork.

He put his big, clumsy hands all over his graphs and charts. He looked under his pads; he indifferently picked through his papers. Brantley wished just to slap his hands away. But he could only watch, helpless, as Prescott callously perused and rearranged what he had taken so much time to perfect.

'What the hell is this?' Prescott asked.

'That's a production performance chart for the western region,' Brantley said, quickly. Then he shrank back, abashed. 'Uh, I would imagine.'

Prescott made a petulant face and tossed a chart aside. Then he picked up what was placed carefully beneath all

140

of the paperwork: something placed to escape the attention of anyone, let alone Prescott himself.

It was an envelope addressed to the big man. It was stuffed with all of Brantley's — and now Christy's — final projections, predictions, conclusions. It was not supposed to be opened. Exposing it now would have been like reading the Oscar winners before the show; it would invalidate everything.

Still, Prescott opened it. And still, Prescott read it.

'Have you ever seen Whitfield, Brantley?' he asked.

'Lots of times. I deliver here every day.'

Prescott noticed what was below his eyes then. He responded with a mixture of deep impatience and fear.

'What is this? Cost breakdown comparisons between our suppliers and the competition's suppliers? Where does he get these things?'

'Available in most quarterly stock reports,' Brantley said, proudly, then again checked himself. 'I hear tell.'

Prescott re-stuffed the envelope and closed it. But he did not put it down on the desk. He handed it to his most lowly and useless messenger.

'Here,' he said to Brantley. 'Take this up to my office, I'll read it later.'

It felt good to have the envelope back in his own hand; Brantley held it tightly. He had no choice, however, but to start for the door and Prescott's place.

He turned around at the door, waiting for Prescott to follow his lead. But Prescott wasn't following. He was interestedly fiddling around the desk again.

Brantley swallowed, trying to be tactful. 'Aren't you coming soon?'

Prescott waved him away.

'Tell Maureen I'll be there soon,' he said, absently.

Brantley waited another minute. 'Soon' wasn't soon enough for him. He turned and went out the door.

As he proceeded dutifully to Prescott's office, he heard

more frightening sounds behind him. He heard Howard Prescott doing some further investigating. With no supervision at all.

CHAPTER TWENTY-FOUR

Brantley wasn't walking long before he bumped into someone else to whom he owed an explanation.

Melrose.

He met his mailroom colleague coming around a corner. Brantley could not know to what lengths his friend — or his friend's leg — had gone to save him from Brady. Melrose, ever the class act, was not talking. He did feel, however, that Brantley owed him some kind of explanation.

'One question,' he said. 'What the hell are you doing?'

'Having a nervous breakdown.'

Brantley walked alongside Melrose, grateful to be at last revealed to someone. He did not offer any more facts and Melrose did not ask for any.

'No wonder,' Melrose said. 'Nothing good can come of this, Brantley. If you get caught, you get canned. If you don't get caught, you become one of them — a suit. It's a no-win situation.'

Brantley heard this advice with interest. But he did not take it; he could not. He had come too far. He was still, after all, Brantley Foster.

'I'm still half a step ahead of them, pal,' he said.

'Yeah, well, when you make it up to the top, don't forget the guys down in the mailroom.'

'I never forget the little people,' Brantley joked.

They looked at each other, further allied than ever. Melrose just watched as Brantley walked ahead of him,

143

getting ahead, leaving him behind but leaving him laughing.

Brantley made it to Prescott's office. He intended to just leave the thing and go — or better yet, find some way *not* to leave the thing. He knew that Prescott could not already be there.

Maureen was typing a transcript from a dictaphone. She looked up, only momentarily. Brantley held up the envelope.

'Mr Prescott asked me to deliver —'

'In there,' Maureen motioned.

She had done so as if someone were expecting him. Brantley was confused. Then he just figured Maureen was distracted, taking dictation as she was.

He went into Prescott's open office. This time, he did not bother to ogle the view. He was too busy trying to figure: should he say he left the envelope or not? Should he say he lost the envelope? Should he . . .

Brantley heard the door close behind him.

He wheeled around. Vera Prescott was standing at the door. Her back was pressing it shut; her arms were crossed at her attractive chest. She smiled a spiderwoman smile.

'Look what room service sent up,' she said.

Brantley swallowed, slowly. Every possible calamity of his young life seemed to be taking place in one afternoon. He thought that life had lousy timing. He thought that Vera had great legs. He thought he was in even greater trouble than he thought.

'Hi,' he said, weakly.

'I suddenly appreciate,' Vera went on, 'why Howard had a sofa put in and a lock installed on the door.'

With that, Vera swiveled ever so slightly. Then with one flick of her fancy fingers, she turned the lock on the door.

She began to slink towards Brantley now, sidle towards him, swim towards him through the office air. She was not intending to shake his hand. Brantley began to back up. Watching her, mesmerized, he backed up as far as he could: smack into Prescott's desk. This was where he stopped. This was where Vera had him.

'He's on his way up,' Brantley stammered, 'any minute now . . . I think he might be armed.'

Vera just smiled at him, to say, Silly Boy. Then she got too close, too close for comfort. She was practically pressed against him, pinning him to the desk.

'Aunt Vera,' Brantley said, 'we have to talk this over.'

Talking was the last thing on Vera's mind. She slowly wrapped her arms around his neck. Her perfume flew into his nose. Brantley felt faint.

But it only reminded him of Christy's natural scent and made things worse.

'Since our last meeting,' Brantley said, 'something has changed.'

Vera was kissing him now; more exactly, she was nibbling him. Her teeth chewed lightly at his neck. Brantley began to feel his knees giving way.

'Yes,' she said, 'your clothes. Nice suit.'

'No, I've become seriously and emotionally involved with someone who isn't my aunt.'

'That's nice.'

Was that all she was going to say? Brantley could not help noticing how intent she was, how irresistible she seemed to find him. It made things harder.

'I don't think it's fair,' he said, 'to lead you on this way.'

Vera shut him up then. She kissed him passionately on the mouth.

Brantley could have gone either way, he knew. He could have stood there and taken it like a man. Or he could have stood there and stopped it like a man. Either way he chose, he would lose something.

Brantley chose.

With just enough force, Brantley unwrapped her arms from around him.

'I can't go on letting you go on this way,' he said.

'There's someone else in my life.'

'There's someone else in my life too,' Vera said. 'Maybe we should introduce your girlfriend to my husband, then everyone would have someone else in his life.'

Very funny, Brantley thought. Vera started for him again. He eluded her arms. In the short time he had, he slipped away from her and to the door.

Vera was right behind him. He made it to the door before she could catch him. He unlocked it. Then he turned to her, with regret, as if to say a final farewell. Vera nodded, sadly.

Then she locked the door again.

'Look,' Brantley said, 'I don't want to have to get rough, but I'll belt you around if I have to.'

That remark got exactly what he thought it might get: a big laugh in his face. Brantley sighed and unlocked the door again. Vera sighed and locked it. Brantley sighed and unlocked it.

'Please, Aunt Vera. If we get caught, I'll get fired. You've got to give me a break.'

He sounded like a little boy, he knew — but one wishing *not* to be naughty. His tone served only to annoy Vera.

'Don't whine, Brantley,' she said. 'Life is short. Before you know it, you'll be forty, wondering where it all went. Enjoy things while you can.'

Brantley was listening to his aunt's little lecture; he did not realize he was also moving. He was being backed up by her as she gave him her passionate pep talk. At the moment her talking ceased, she backed him far enough back to send Brantley onto the sofa.

Vera knelt beside him. She grabbed his shoulders and kissed him again, hard. Brantley began to feel too tired to fight. They were situated this way — Brantley sitting, Vera kneeling — when they both heard the door open.

Howard Prescott entered.

146

Vera turned slowly around. Brantley's eyes grew to three times their normal size. His uncle looked down at the two of them in such a curious position. Prescott did not know what reaction exactly to have.

'What's this?' he asked, purely confused.

Vera seemed to look down at herself: her hands holding Brantley by the shoulders, kneeling solicitously by him, as if attending to him. She immediately had an explanation.

'He fainted,' she said.

'Fainted?' her husband said.

Vera looked at poor, woozy Brantley for verification. Brantley did the best he could.

'Sort of,' he said.

'Actually,' Vera expanded, 'he hit his head.'

'It was like fainting,' Brantley agreed. 'Knocked out.'

'Hit his head on what?' Prescott asked.

'The ceiling,' said Brantley.

'The floor,' said Vera.

'Which one?' asked their husband and uncle.

'Neither,' Brantley admitted.

'Both,' Vera insisted.

There was a long, unpleasant pause before Prescott exploded.

'What the hell happened?'

Brantley sat up, thinking quickly. He looked around the room for any object that would give him inspiration. Then he looked back at Vera.

'Well, I walked in and found this beautiful woman,' Brantley said, 'who I had never seen before in my life. When I found out she was my Aunt Vera —'

'He was so excited,' Vera said, helpfully, 'that his blood pressure shot up.'

There was another long, equally unpleasant pause ended again by Prescott.

'And he hit his head *on the ceiling*?'

Brantley nodded, amazed himself. 'It was Ripley's.'

147

Prescott looked as if he were about to ask, Who's Ripley? but kept quiet. He looked at his wife for further developments.

'Then he fell and hit his head on the floor,' she said.

'Out like a light,' Brantley said. 'Deliriously and fevered, I crawled to the sofa —'

'And I rushed to his aid.'

'And you walked in.'

Spoiling everything, Brantley thought, but also saving my life. Or at least my love life.

Vera was coy with her husband now. She stepped forward and teased a little with his tie.

'Shame on you, Howard,' she said, 'for not telling me our nephew was working for the company.'

Prescott made a face at Vera, not falling for her flirtation. He moved away from her, from Brantley, from the whole situation and sat down at his desk.

'Our nephew works for the company,' he told her. 'Now, I've got a million problems to deal with here today, why are you here?'

Brantley thought this tone awfully brusque with his own wife, but Vera seemed used to it. She did not bat an eye. Her voice, however, betrayed both subtle hatred and hurt.

'Lunch,' she said. 'We were supposed to have lunch.'

'I had my lunch,' Prescott said. 'You don't seem to realize —'

Vera could not completely contain herself now; her tone became curt and vaguely threatening.

'I realize, Howard. You won't mind if Brantley takes me to lunch so we can get acquainted?'

'Fine,' Prescott said.

Brantley stood up, instinctively, trapped.

'No!' he cried. 'I can't do that!' He saw both heads turn curiously towards him. 'I mean, I . . . have to go to the funeral.'

'You said you already went,' Prescott reminded him.

148

'Oh, right . . .' Brantley bowed his head. 'In my grief, I forgot.'

There was a stalemate. No one was in any mood to challenge Brantley; he was in no condition to back up his story further. They all just stood there, waiting for a way out.

Finally, Vera came up with one.

'Howard, why don't we bring Brantley out to the house for the party this weekend? I mean, he *is* family.'

Prescott did not even seem to consider it. 'Fine, fine. Whatever you want.'

Brantley felt a chill run down his spine. Their house? Where he and Vera had first — met? He did not think he could deal with such a thing.

He saw a change come over Prescott now. The boss had suddenly paid attention to the party idea. He was more than indifferent to it, more even than approving; he seemed intrigued.

'Yes,' Prescott said now. 'You know, that might be a *very* good idea. We should take . . . better care of our nephew.'

Brantley seemed to be out-voted. He could only make a last, lame plea to be excused.

'I don't think I would fit in, Aunt Vera.'

'You *do* fit in,' she said, blithely. 'I'll make sure you have a wonderful time. I'll spend every moment with you.'

This prospect intrigued and gratified Prescott more. He seemed almost as excited as Vera — for obviously different reasons, Brantley thought. He could only force an inferior imitation of a smile upon his face and nod.

'All right,' Prescott clapped his hands. 'It's settled. Now — can I get back to work here?'

With an aunt's intimacy, Vera linked her arm with Brantley's and led him out of the office. Brantley could have been mistaken but he thought he heard Prescott whistling happily and expectantly as they exited.

149

'It'll be nice,' Vera whispered, 'to have a playmate for the weekend.'

CHAPTER TWENTY-FIVE

The party was at the end of the week. It could also mean the end of Brantley's job, the end of his career, the end of his masquerade, the end of his relationship with Christy.

All the rest of it he could deal with — sort of — but losing Christy would be a blow from which he might not recover. And she had seemed so cold to him before, she had kissed him off for the weekend. Maybe it was better this way for now; how could he explain what his own weekend plans were?

Brantley felt the whole thing was coming to a head. He did not know how much longer he could maintain his two lives. Maybe he should just forget about it and work his way up the ladder like everybody else.

Brantley thought a minute.

Nah.

The day before the big day, Brantley received a strange directive in the mailroom. He was to proceed to the office of the Pemrose leader, his own uncle, the corporate cuckold, Howard Prescott.

Brantley had been hoping to avoid Prescott until the party. He was hoping to avoid him during the party. But he could not avoid a direct order to come see him — not in his office but in the Pemrose gym.

He came upon Prescott panting. The older man was in his sweat-suit, running in place on a treadmill. That's good, Brantley thought, keep running in place, we'll all be safer that way.

'You wanted to see me, sir?' he asked, meekly.

Prescott looked over at him, suspiciously. Brantley tried to remain calm. Maybe he could just jack the machine up to high speed, send Prescott flying, and make a break for it.

'Yes, Brantley. I want you to know I've been watching you very closely lately.'

'You have . . . ?'

Just one spin of the dial, Brantley thought, and the old guy will be propelled through the wall. His fingers twitched anxiously at his side.

'I know everything that you've been up to.'

'You do?'

Maybe he should just stop it suddenly; Prescott would go head-first onto the floor, and Brantley could run for it.

'Everything.'

Brantley thought violence would be pointless. He might as well own up to everything. He had a great feeling of relief.

'Well, I'd like to explain . . .'

'I know, for example,' Prescott said, 'that you've worked hard in the mailroom. You've kept your eyes open and your nose clean. You've stayed out of trouble.'

Brantley started. He had an even greater feeling of relief. The only thing better than admitting everything was not having to admit anything. He was glad he had been interrupted when he had.

'Yes, sir?'

Brantley had some inkling of what Prescott wanted and it filled him with incredible dread. What could he do for his uncle that would not be seamy or immoral? Not much. He took a deep breath.

'We'll talk about it while we work out,' Prescott suggested. 'Do you like to sweat, Brantley?'

I must, Brantley thought. I seem to do enough of it.

This kind of sweating was not what he had meant. Within minutes, he and his uncle were panting beside each other, man to man, riding stationary bicycles.

Brantley had a fantasy of riding the bike off its blocks and pedaling back to Kansas, but it passed. Like most of his other employees, Brantley had a hard time keeping Prescott's pace.

'We're both adults, right?' Prescott asked. 'Men of the world. I imagine you've had your share of experiences with girls.'

I've had some of the same experiences with them as you have, Brantley thought. But he only gave the expected reply to any such rhetorical question.

'Well . . .'

'I don't want to hear about it,' Prescott said, bluntly. 'Your Aunt Vera seems to have taken an instant liking to you.'

'I . . . hadn't noticed.'

'It was obvious. I'm sure she'd like to get to know you a lot better.'

Keep pedaling, Brantley thought. Move all of your embarrassment and discomfort down into your feet and ride. Zen and the art of infidelity.

'I'd like to encourage that,' Prescott continued. 'I'd like you to spend lots of time with Vera at the party this weekend.'

Brantley stopped pedaling. He turned, confused, to his much more worldly uncle. What did Prescott have in mind?

Prescott stopped pedaling, too, then. He looked at Brantley as if to ask, Okay? Brantley looked back at him as if to say, Uh, sure.

After such a strenuous workout, manly men had to consume a hearty meal. Prescott next took Brantley to his own private dining room for a lunch that differed — just a tad — from the Pemrose cafeteria fare.

Brantley ate ravenously of the *nouvelle cuisine*. Whatever it was, it was delicious.

'Men like us can't be locked down to one woman, Brantley,' Prescott said, chewing. 'We need variety. It

153

keeps us young, energetic, competitive. You get my meaning? Of course you do.'

Brantley thought Prescott wanted him to take notes or something. Instead, he concentrated on some delicious little squiggly vegetables.

'We're men of the world here,' Prescott insisted. 'Now, a problem has developed. I have a friend. A companion —'

'A girl.'

Prescott pressed on. 'She's been getting antsy lately and wants me to leave my wife. But I'm not going to leave my wife, not for her or for anyone.'

Brantley put down a heaping forkful of veggies. He was beginning to get the picture here. He was beginning to lose his appetite.

The two men of the world next took a leisurely stroll around the corridors, working off their sumptuous meal. Prescott surveyed the Pemrose halls as if casually checking on his kingdom. He smiled benevolently at passing underlings. He winked at comely secretaries. And he spoke in a whisper to Brantley.

'I need a little time to get the situation under control again. You understand?'

Make him sweat for it, Brantley thought. Make him spell it out in big block letter flash cards.

'Not altogether.'

Prescott sighed, a bit impatient with his fellow stud.

'I'm inviting her out to the party this weekend. We're going to spend a little time together.'

Brantley had an idea that's what this all had been leading to. He gave no indication, however. He looked, innocently, at Prescott, forcing him to explain even more.

'That's why I need you to keep Vera occupied as much as possible. Get the picture?'

Brantley turned a little pale, now that the truth was out. It was one thing to sleep with someone's wife. It was

154

another to have the husband's permission to do so, no matter how blind he was. It was all getting a little too cozy — and unsavory. He would have to make his regrets.

'Wide screen,' Brantley said then. 'But the problem is I've got some big plans this weekend and I don't see how I could —'

'Fine. I won't forget this favor, believe me.'

'Oh, no. I can't. You see —'

'Great, then it's all settled. I'm keeping my eye out for some rapid advancement for you, Brantley. You seem to be a young man with a lot on the ball.'

His mission over, without so much as a goodbye, Prescott breezed off into his office. He left Brantley standing, open-mouthed, alone in the hall.

Brantley shook his head. The things *he* did to get ahead were no match for the things other people would have him do. Impersonating Whitfield suddenly seemed a jolly, benign caprice compared to the sordid intrigues of Prescott.

Well, he wouldn't do it, that was all. Keep his wife busy — *very* busy — so Prescott could be busy with his babe? No way. This weekend was shaping up as a French farce with only the betrayals and none of the laughs.

Still, he wasn't exactly sure what he would do to avoid it. He wished he could speak to Christy about it but Christy wasn't talking to him. When it came to love and money, life could be one big gray area.

If his mother could only see him now.

CHAPTER TWENTY-SIX

The Prescotts certainly knew how to throw a party.

Their large estate was attractively dressed for the weekend, with furniture and furnishings even brighter and more elegant than usual. Tables had been set up with fancy little hors d'oeuvres on them; waiters from catering companies carried about trays with drinks.

It was clearly not going to be just business. Executives lolled about the pool; others floated in it, languidly; still others aggressively shot balls at each other across the backyard tennis court.

Brantley showed up late but he showed up.

He almost decided not to. But at the last minute, his curiosity, his ambition — not to mention his fear — got the better of him. He arrived with some feeling that this would be a make-or-break occasion.

Brantley walked stiffly to the backyard, where the festivities seemed the most vocal. He looked around at many familiar faces from the company — Thomas, Ferguson, et al. Then he saw the face of a woman who controlled the company — and loved to control Brantley.

Vera was in the midst of a group of admirers, laughing gaily, highball in hand, like a wife in a Noel Coward play. When she turned, she saw Brantley and immediately became deaf to her companions.

She excused herself, charmingly, and sashayed across the lawn to her young guest. She reached out a demure, perfectly manicured hand to him.

'Brantley, darling, you're late,' she said. 'I'm so

157

pleased to see you. There are some very important people here I'm anxious for you to meet.'

She took his arm, lovable auntie, boss' wife, and pulled him purposefully towards the house. Brantley wore a mortified smile as they moved.

On their way, they passed many an executive who had seen Brantley causing commotion in meetings. They all seemed to be impressed that he had arrived — figuratively and literally — by being invited to Prescott's.

'Good to see you, Whitfield,' one said.

There was a pause. Brantley was praying Vera had not heard the man in all the surrounding noise. Vera, however, rarely missed a trick.

'Whitfield?' she asked.

'My middle name,' Brantley said, swiftly. 'Brantley Whitfield —'

'Hi, Carlton,' another executive said.

'Carlton Foster.'

Vera just looked at him, nonplussed.

'You go by all those names?'

Brantley nodded, sagely. 'I'm many things to many people.'

Vera smiled. Her hold of his arm grew tighter. 'Well, you're just one thing to me.'

Brantley blushed, deeply, and shook his head. Ah, Vera, ever the romantic.

The two of them passed the pool then. Standing near it was a serene-seeming older man. He surveyed all before him with gentle condescension.

'That's Roland Owens,' Vera whispered, 'of the Federal Security Bank. I'm going to make sure you spend a few moments with him. And see the funny little fat man playing tennis?'

Brantley glanced over. Sure enough, the man swiping at the ball was fat, little and, depending on taste, funny.

'Yes. So?'

'Vernon S. Fletcher of Wall Street. He absolutely reeks

158

with power and influence.'

His game definitively reeks, anyway, Brantley thought, as the man hobbled after a lob. Brantley looked away from him then to a suave type watching the game, boredly.

'Who's the tall guy with all the girls around him?'

'McMartin of First National. A bachelor. His money is so attractive, even if he isn't.'

Brantley nodded. When he turned around again, he was staring into the cold, obedient eyes of a butler. They were at the house.

'Show Mr Foster to his room,' Vera told him.

As if being given up to his jailer, Vera turned Brantley over to her servant. The man nodded, coolly, and took the nervous young executive inside.

Brantley did not know it but he was being watched. Through a beautiful, clear picture window, Christy had her eye on him.

She was standing in the spacious library of the Prescott home. She was standing beside the man who professed to have read all of its books — but had not — Howard Prescott.

Christy was shocked to see Brantley; it had never occurred to her he would be there. She was even more unsettled to see the proprietary way Prescott's vampire wife had dug her claws in him. She felt both protective of Brantley, furious at Vera, and unable to escape Howard to do much about it.

Prescott was busy leafing through his briefcase. He soon came up with his treasure: the notes that Christy had pilfered from Whitfield. He shuffled through them, appreciatively.

'Here are Whitfield's notes,' he said. 'Impressive.'

Christy heard the words with great discomfort. She gave only an indifferent shrug in reply.

'Thank you.'

Christy wasn't turned his way but she could hear

159

Prescott moving towards her. Within a second, she felt his hands fall gently onto her shoulders. She saw Brantley and Vera entering the house.

She shook Howard off.

'This is a business trip, remember?' she snapped.

Christy looked coldly into Howard's eyes. But as always, all she saw was amused patience: he would wait her out.

She turned, quickly, and walked from the room.

Brantley soon grew bored. He wandered, unoccupied, around the house. He watched tennis games; he drank; he sat around the pool. Against his better judgment, he began to wonder when the problems would start.

As he was drinking by the pool, he saw Prescott leading a parade of about a dozen executives. They all marched dutifully inside. Then through a window, Brantley saw them take their places at a long table.

A hand touched his shoulder from behind. He turned. Vera was standing there, solicitously.

'What are they meeting about?' he asked.

'This takeover nonsense,' Vera shrugged. 'It's all so boring. Be patient, dear — someday, you'll be one of them.'

'Sooner than anyone thinks,' Brantley said.

'That's the spirit.'

Vera found time to blow a little in his ear. Then she was called away by another group of guests.

Brantley just stood there, transfixed by the meeting. He saw Prescott check his watch, as if waiting for someone tardy. Then he looked up, relieved; this last person had arrived. Brantley caught his breath.

It was Christy.

CHAPTER TWENTY-SEVEN

Brantley figured he would have as many problems as he wanted soon.

He watched as the meeting progressed; it was a silent movie about big business. He saw Prescott look with impatience at Thomas. He saw Thomas open his obsequious mouth.

'I think you'll all find that these cutbacks are exactly what the doctor ordered if we're going to remain on a solid enough footing to fight this takeover.'

'I've already seen the report in a preliminary stage,' Prescott nodded, 'and I'm satisfied that it does the job.'

Thomas smiled, like a boy being patted by his Dad. All the other executives purred, with satisfaction. All except Christy.

She could not keep silent now. Prescott's smug face made her want to scream. Whitfield's presence at the party made her want to speak up.

'I know this isn't on the agenda, but —'

'Excuse me?' Prescott said, surprised. 'You have something to add that isn't in the report?'

She nodded. 'I've given a lot of careful thought to this report. I know I signed my name to it, but the simple fact is I don't believe it's the right answer any more.'

Thomas was crestfallen. 'But we all agreed . . . '

'I don't agree any more,' Christy said, with force. 'One person in this company has the right answer and that person is Carlton Whitfield.'

She took a deep breath. It had really hit the fan now.

Prescott wrinkled his nose, with distaste.

'The elusive Mr Whitfield again,' he said.

'We've been over that,' Thomas said, quickly. 'Expansion — it's out of the question.'

Arguments broke out from one end of the table to the other. Christy was forced to defend herself; she found she did more than a capable job. Even with Prescott staring, furiously, at her.

His eyes darting through the window to the meeting, Brantley tried to maintain a conversation outside. It was with the three men Vera thought could do so much for him: serene Owens, fat and funny Fletcher and magnetic McMartin.

'What people have forgotten,' Brantley said, distractedly, 'is that mergers were originally devised for the common good of all parties. But raiders have corrupted that intent and too many people get hurt.'

Owens took umbrage. 'You're quite right, young man, but —'

Brantley saw the meeting breaking up; he saw Prescott stand with what seemed rage. He immediately stood up himself.

'Excuse me, sir. Pardon me. I'll be back.'

He heard the harrumphs of powerful men not used to being interrupted. A few months ago, Brantley would never have dreamed of interrupting them. That was before he met Christy.

Brantley cut quickly into the house. He looked to the left and right. Then he saw an unforgettable blonde form passing quickly by.

Christy turned. She saw him. A big surprised smile formed upon her lips.

'Carlton! I don't believe it! What are you doing here?'

Brantley did not know that her surprise was just as phony as his own. Still, he played his own part to the hilt.

'It's a party, isn't it?' he said, suavely. 'Carlton Whitfield will go anywhere to attend a party.'

162

There was a pause. Then Brantley threw caution to the wind. He swept Christy up in his arms. When he stopped swinging her, he gave her a big kiss.

'I'm glad you're here,' she whispered.

They danced together that evening. The Prescotts had hired a rock band for 'the young people,' and Brantley and Christy were making the most of it. They might as well have been alone on the dance floor, as they moved in and out of each other's arms.

They certainly paid no attention to the inside of the house, which Prescott was now patrolling. The boss pulled aside a young executive, who was watching the proceedings out the window, longingly.

'Have you seen Christy?' Prescott asked.

'Yes, sir,' the lonely young man said. 'She's dancing with Whitfield.'

Prescott started. 'Whitfield? What's *he* doing here? He wasn't invited.'

Angrily, Prescott proceeded to comb the rest of the house, turning his back on the picture window and the dance floor.

The music became slower and more romantic; so did Brantley and Christy. They swayed almost imperceptibly together. Both had their eyes closed; neither saw Prescott approaching.

Brantley felt him, though. Suddenly a big hand had grabbed his shoulder and separated him from Christy.

Brantley stared, stammering, into Prescott's angry, slightly drunken eyes.

'Excuse us just a minute, Christy,' Prescott said.

Christy looked confusedly after them as the Pemrose boss and the man she knew as Whitfield disappeared to the edge of the crowd.

Prescott cornered him then, with a deeply accusatory gaze. Silently, Brantley began inventing excuses by the handful.

'Did you know Whitfield is here?' Prescott asked.

163

Brantley was dazed by the inquiry. Wasn't *he* Whitfield? Who was Whitfield? 'Uh — he was earlier — but I think he left.'

'No.' Prescott was sure. 'Somebody saw him a few minutes ago, dancing with Christy. I've got my reasons for this, Brantley — I want you to stay close to Christy and keep Whitfield away from her. Will you do that?'

Brantley almost laughed in Prescott's face. But instead he took on a solemn 'responsible' tone. 'Certainly.'

Prescott was relieved. 'Good boy. I'm counting on you.' He clapped Brantley on the arm in a manly sort of way. Then, winking, he was off.

Shaking his head with amazement, Brantley rejoined Christy near the dance floor.

'What was that all about?' she asked.

'He told me to stay close to you.'

Christy's eyebrows rose. 'He told you that?'

'Guess he thinks we're a good couple.'

Brantley smiled. But Christy only looked pensive, because she knew better than he — and knew Prescott better than anyone.

CHAPTER TWENTY-EIGHT

Everyone had a romantic evening in mind that night. Brantley figured he would sneak out of his room and into Christy's room. Christy figured she would sneak into his. Prescott thought he might manage a little midnight dalliance with Christy. Vera thought Brantley might afford her some fun after lights out.

Unfortunately, all of them had the idea at the same time.

Brantley began. Putting a robe on over his pajamas, he stood before a mirror. He doused himself with cologne — with too much, it turned out. He combed his hair several times. Then he turned and tiptoed out into the hall.

Christy was slipping on her robe at the same moment. She peeked out of her room, saw the coast was clear, and then proceeded on her quest for love.

Love was an exalted name for what Prescott had in mind. He looked over at his sleeping wife and checked her out.

'Vera?' he whispered. 'Are you awake?'

He received no answer. Smiling a little to himself, he slipped out of bed. He walked with the utmost care to the door. Just as his hand gripped the knob, his left foot slammed into a stool.

Stifling his screams, hopping on one foot, Prescott limped his way out of the bedroom. With his attention so diverted, he could not see that Vera was watching him with one wise eye open.

Christy, meanwhile, was halfway to Brantley's room

when she saw Prescott — hopping like a fool — leave his room. She immediately slipped through the nearest door.

It turned out to be Art Thomas' bedroom. Her heart pounding, Christy looked over with terror at the sleeping form of the brown-nosing executive. He had a pleasant smile on his face, as if dreaming of serving someone.

Behind him in the hall, Prescott heard Thomas' door opening. Trying to forget his pain, concentrating on panic instead, he ducked through the nearest door himself.

The head of Pemrose was now hiding in a broom closet.

Brantley, carrying a rose he had plucked from a vase, sensed in the hall Prescott's proximity. It wasn't hard: he heard a clatter of falling brooms and mops. He took it as a signal to move as fast as he could.

Christy opened Thomas' door just a crack. Suddenly, in the hall, she saw another unwelcome sight: Vera Prescott. Christy closed the door again, quickly. The noise was enough to disturb Thomas, who mumbled a little, upset, in his sleep.

Christy opened the door one more time. Now she saw Howard Prescott emerging stealthily from a closet. She closed the door again.

Brantley, of course, had no idea Christy was fraternizing — however reluctantly — with Art Thomas. He was too busy opening *her* door and with debonair ease, slipping inside.

He was about to announce himself when he noticed: Christy was missing. Her bed was rumpled but unoccupied. Confused, he opened the door — and saw Howard Prescott limping on a bad ankle towards him. He shut the door again. He protected himself further: he locked it.

Brantley smiled, relieved, as he heard Prescott rattling the knob to no avail. What could *he* want in Christy's room, anyway?

Prescott cursed outside in the hall. He was not about to be deterred by any locked door; let that little minx

Christy play hard to get. He walked, haltingly, down the stairs to find a key.

Christy looked out of Thomas' room one last time. Now the coast was clear. She moved briskly in the direction of Whitfield's bedroom. As she did, she was deaf to two sounds: the bathroom door opening and Vera Prescott — newly hidden — peeking out.

Brantley listened hard at Christy's door. He heard no more evidence of Prescott's presence. He unlocked the door and looked out: sure enough, the boss was gone away. Brantley turned to make sure everything was as he had found it. He saw something peculiar sitting on a chair.

It was Christy's bag. *It* was not peculiar but there was something sticking from it: a pack of papers.

Brantley quickly locked the door again. He tiptoed over the few steps to investigate. He pulled the pack further out of the bag. Then he read the papers, with ever-increasing outrage.

Christy had stolen his notes. All this time, he had thought they were working together and now he knew: she was working for Prescott. No wonder she had been so cold to him before. No wonder she seemed so willing to be kind to him now.

For her part, Christy had entered Brantley's room. She found no such incriminating information; she found nothing at all. She smiled, realizing that Whitfield had probably gone to *her* room. Great minds love alike, she thought. She opened the door to join him — and immediately closed it again. Vera Prescott was approaching.

Christy hid in the shadows of Whitfield's room. She held her breath as the door creaked open and Vera — creaky herself, Christy thought — looked in. Disappointed, she soon went away. Christy waited a minute, for safety; then she, too, took her leave.

At the same moment, Brantley was flinging down his own notes in despair. He had trusted her and she had betrayed him. He would never lie to *her* like that. Brantley thought of his masquerade then. But that was not as bad as this!

Brantley heard someone turn a key in the lock.

Cursing, he stuffed the papers quickly back in Christy's bag. The labored breathing outside told him it was either Prescott or a water buffalo. He looked here and there for a place to hide. Finally, he had no choice but to bite the bullet.

Brantley leaped into the bed.

He pulled the covers up over his head. He gave an adequate imitation of someone sleeping. He heard Prescott enter. Brantley hoped he would just take his notes or whatever he wanted and leave.

But the boss had other ideas.

Prescott slowly sidled into the sack beside him. He threw a well-muscled arm across Brantley's body. Then he snorted into his ear.

'Christy? I only have a few minutes . . .'

Brantley almost screamed. Christy and Prescott — *he* was the married man!

Prescott moved his hand over to Brantley's face. Brantley immediately slapped it hard — just as Christy should have the first time, he thought.

Prescott pulled away, like a big admonished lion. Then he started cutely wheedling.

'Oh, honey, don't be that way. I know you're mad, but think of all the things we've meant to each other.'

Brantley rolled his eyes. How had she ever fallen for such stuff? What women wouldn't do — and what Christy would! Brantley felt like placing the pillow over Prescott's face.

Instead he simply listened to more 'sweet talk.'

'I want to marry you, Christy. We could go up to Boston next weekend and plan everything.'

Prescott now placed a sincere, compassionate hand on Brantley's shoulder.

'What do you say, honey? Will you marry me?'

There was a long pause. Brantley lay there, steaming, wondering how Christy could be low enough to deceive him — *and* stupid enough to believe Prescott. He decided to give Prescott an answer he would long remember, regardless of the impact on his own career. Sometimes success was not measured in dollar signs.

Brantley sat up. He glared right at Prescott.

'I wouldn't marry you if you were the last man on Earth,' he said.

Prescott opened his mouth, stunned. But he had no time to reply before the door of the room suddenly banged open.

Christy stood, doused in the light from the hall. She stared, astonished, at the two men in bed.

Then Vera was right behind her. She looked at Christy; Christy looked at her; both of them looked at Prescott and Brantley. Then Vera shouted what all of them were thinking.

'What the hell is going on?'

CHAPTER TWENTY-NINE

The party had turned suddenly into a pajama party.

Prescott decided he did not want to attend any more. He jumped out of bed. Then he turned viciously on Brantley.

'Brantley, what're you doing in Christy's bed?' Prescott said.

'I'm talking to *you*, Howard!' Vera said.

'Who's Brantley?' Christy wondered.

'Brantley's the guy who just found his stolen notes in your purse,' Brantley explained, loudly.

'Those are Whitfield's notes,' Prescott said, 'and they're *not* stolen! He gave them to me himself!'

Brantley turned on Prescott. 'And you were so grateful, you climbed into bed with him and asked him to marry you!'

'What are you talking about?' Prescott asked, confused. 'I climbed into bed with you!'

Vera stepped forward now, pointing to Christy. 'But you thought you were climbing into bed with *her*!'

'When I came in,' Christy protested, 'he was in bed with Whitfield!'

'Whitfield?' Prescott said. 'He wasn't even here!'

Christy was the one to point now, at Brantley. 'Are you blind? Then who's that?'

'That's Brantley!' Prescott replied.

'Brantley?' Christy said, quietly.

Brantley could feel his heart pounding hard now. But Vera had no time for mistaken identities; she was more interested in punishing her husband.

'So this is the bimbo you've been screwing around with at the office, right?' she said.

'Who are you calling a bimbo?'Christy said.

Brantley could not resist. 'If the shoe fits.'

Christy glared at him. 'What's *that* supposed to mean?'

Brantley waved his stolen notes in her face. 'Why didn't you just ask for these? I would have given them to you.'

Christy shrank a bit from him now. Her tone was quieter, more unsure. 'I was going to tell you about that. It happened before I really knew you.'

'So when we were in bed, that was all official James Bond company stuff, right?'

Christy cringed. All of her worst nightmares — inevitably, she knew — were coming true. 'No!'

Prescott confronted her now. 'You were in bed with Brantley?'

'Sure,' Brantley answered for her. 'She was taking microfilm pictures of the whole thing.'

It was Vera's turn to interrogate Christy; she did it, however, with only a relative's dismay. 'What were you doing in bed with my nephew?'

'Whitfield's your nephew?' Christy asked.

Prescott was practically apoplectic. 'Why do you keep calling him Whitfield? This is Brantley Foster. He works in the mailroom.'

'The mailroom!' Christy turned bright red. 'You mean he's not an executive?'

There was a long pause. All of them swiveled slowly to get a good look at the man who now stood with an uneasy smile.

'Let me get this straight,' Prescott said. 'Brantley is Whitfield?'

Brantley threw up his hands. There were a million different lies he could have told, a million different excuses he could have made. But enough was enough.

172

Besides, a room full of adults in their pajamas encouraged honesty.

'That's right,' he said. 'Brantley is Whitfield, Whitfield is Brantley.'

Everyone was shocked — except Vera. She couldn't have cared less.

'And Christy is the bimbo,' she said. 'Now that we've had Mouseketeer-roll call, I'll just go call my lawyer!'

'Now wait a minute,' Prescott said, protectively. 'Christy's not the bimbo I was screwing around with at the office.'

'People better stop calling me a bimbo,' Christy warned.

'It was an entirely different bimbo altogether!'

'That's just fine,' Vera said. 'How many bimbos would you say there were?'

Prescott blushed — a first for him, Brantley thought. 'I misspoke myself. I meant to say there weren't any bimbos at all.'

'Except Christy,' Brantley threw in.

'Right,' Prescott said. 'I mean — no!'

'The question is,' Brantley said, 'who *else* did she sleep with to get to the top?'

Christy turned then, all of her shame and dismay turned to anger. Brantley thought he might have gone too far; then he figured there were no longer any boundaries; who cared? But Christy cared. She grabbed a nearby vase of flowers. She picked it up.

Christy hurled it across the room at Brantley.

Brantley dodged. The thing shattered against the wall.

'Listen,' she said, 'whatever I did was my business, not yours.'

'You mean it was company business, don't you?'

'That's right. And that's all it was — business!'

'Well, I'll tell you something, honey, you sure know your job!'

With that, Brantley turned and stormed out of the

173

room. This whole thing — success, ambition, making something out of yourself — had become so rancid he wanted no part of it. There was nothing wrong with Kansas.

Christy, too, had had her fill. She grabbed her suitcase and began throwing stuff into it. Who *were* these men to sit in judgment on her? Some mailroom boy with big ideas? Some boss with his brains in his pants?

The Prescotts just watched 'the young people' making tracks. Then they, too — at a safe distance from each other — left the room.

The other guests of the party heard some strange noises that night. They heard several cars starting up outside at the same time. They heard some familiar voices saying some unfamiliar things.

If any looked out the window, they could have seen Carlton Whitfield and Christy Welles, both carrying suitcases, standing and screaming at each other in the driveway.

'What's your hurry?' Brantley was saying. 'Prescott will be out in a minute!'

'Go to hell, Whitfield!' Christy was responding. 'Or whatever the hell your name is!'

'Brantley J. Foster! Remember it! I'm still going places in this town!'

'Back to Kansas, that's where you belong!'

If the guests kept looking — and how could they not? — they would have seen two more Pemrose people, *the* Pemrose people: Howard Prescott and his wife. They came out on the tarmac. He was holding a suitcase; she was bearing a tennis racquet and a grudge.

'You forgot your tennis racquet, Howard!' Vera was shouting.

She hurled an expensive Prince racquet right at his head. Prescott moved, barely averting a concussion.

'I won't be back, Vera!' he shouted back. 'I've had it with you forever!'

174

'This is going to cost you, Howard! Oh, is this going to cost you!'

With that, Prescott got into his car. Christy slammed the door of her own vehicle. Brantley was already starting up his car.

The three pulled out at exactly the same time. If anyone watching could bear to look, he would have seen three Pemrose cars — specially assigned for the weekend — smash into each other.

'What the hell are you doing?' Prescott yelled.

'Get out of my way, Goddamn it!' Brantley shouted back.

Christy went into reverse. She peeled away with a squeal of tires. But Prescott was extricating himself, too; Christy rammed right into him again.

'Are you crazy?' Prescott cried.

'Watch me do it again, bastard!' she answered.

Christy backed up just to ram Prescott once more. Prescott's face turned the color of fire. Then he floored the gas and took off. Christy followed close behind him, blowing her horn all the way.

Shaking her head, Vera Prescott was seen to walk back into the house. Whitfield was the last to drive away — though someone could have sworn he had called himself Brantley.

CHAPTER THIRTY

On Monday, Melrose helped Brantley pack.

They threw all of his charts into boxes, folded up graphs, pulled down diagrams. Brantley tried not to think about the disappointment as he returned Whitfield's office to the empty space it had been. He just tried to think of getting *this* job done, the job of clearing it all away.

Melrose merely shook his head, with a sad smile, as he worked. Something had to give, he had always figured. It was too bad it was Brantley's job that gave.

Jean stood in the doorway, watching the action. She stared at her boss, who had never really existed.

'You mean,' she said, 'I was working for a guy from the mailroom? You're not an executive?'

'He's too good to be an executive,' Melrose said.

'Disappointed?' Brantley asked.

'Yes,' Jean answered. 'I was having fun on this job. You had all this energy, all these crazy ideas — and you kept taking off your pants! I don't want you to leave.'

This made Brantley smile; he was surprised anything could. To thank her for that — and for everything else — he took a plant from the window ledge. He handed it to her.

'Something to remember me by,' he said.

Brantley stood there a second, near tears. Melrose gave him a little tap on the arm.

'Hey, why are you looking so sad?'

'I don't know. I just wanted it to turn out better.'

'The job — or the girl?'

Brantley turned. Melrose was looking at him with great knowingness. Brantley shrugged him off, abashed.

'The job. To hell with the girl.'

'You sound real convincing, pal,' Melrose smiled. 'Well, look at it this way. For a few weeks, you sat up here in the lofty atmosphere of the big cheeses with a new view of Manhattan and a clean lunch room to eat in. You did more in two months than most people do in a lifetime.'

'Yeah. I'm gonna miss it.'

'The job — or the girl?'

Brantley did not answer this time. He just turned his face away.

Brantley carried a large box out in the corridor. He was walking to the elevator when the flaps sprang up in his face. His vision was obscured; he pressed the flaps down again.

Christy was standing there.

She was carrying her own box. She looked at him the same way he looked at her: with contempt. Each was like a dog defending its own territory. They both wished no more trespassing on their hearts.

'Going back home?' Christy asked, snidely.

'No, I'm not going back home,' Brantley said, with a sneer. 'I came to New York to succeed.'

'Well, I hear there's an opening in the mailroom.'

'Look who's talking. You're just as unemployed as I am.'

'Not for long. I have contacts all over town.'

'Sure. There'll always be another guy like Prescott to take you under his wing.'

Christy was made silent then. Her eyes filled with tears. She fought them back. Then she pushed out a retort.

'Low blow, Foster,' she said. 'Dirty pool.'

Brantley was surprised to hear his real name on

178

Christy's lips. But she had said it so imperiously — executive to underling — that it infuriated him.

'I call them as I see them,' he said.

'And you're perfect, right? You never make a mistake.'

'I never slept with the boss.'

'No, you slept with the boss' wife.'

It was Brantley's turn to feel stung now. His affair with Vera had gone unmentioned during the shouting match on the weekend. But Christy didn't get where she was by missing signals. Why doesn't the elevator come? he wondered.

'She seduced me,' he said.

'And he seduced me. What's the difference?'

'I couldn't help it. You went willingly.'

'I see. And you were tied up in chains, is that it?'

Brantley almost laughed. Vera just hadn't had time for *that*. 'The difference is . . . '

What *was* the difference? He didn't know — and luckily, he did not have to. The elevator arrived.

Brantley and Christy slowly maneuvered themselves and their belongings inside.

'And I'm the one who thought you were a nice guy with sharp ideas. It turns out —'

'Wait a minute. I *am* a nice guy with bright ideas.'

'You're a rat. You lied to me, deceived me, then acted as judge and jury in a situation you know nothing about.'

'I know enough about it to figure out you were spying on me, using sex as a weapon and stealing all my ideas.'

The car was just sitting there. One of them had to volunteer to press the 'Close Door' button. It was a contest of wills, like everything else now. Finally, both reached forward at the same time.

'Well, I won't be spying on you any more.'

'No, you won't, because if I ever see you coming my way, I'll turn and run so fast, you'll never —'

'You won't have to turn and run, because I wouldn't go

near you if you were the last man on Earth . . . '

Christy's finger was first to hit the button. The doors closed upon them.

When the doors opened again, a waiting crowd in the lobby saw a nice sight: a young man and woman in each other's arms. Forty-three floors is a long drop; hatred, pride and hurt feelings can fall away during the ride.

Brantley glanced over at the expectant riders. He gave them a sympathetic look.

'Sorry,' he told them. 'This car is full.'

He pressed 'Close Door' again. Going down in the world could be pleasant indeed.

CHAPTER THIRTY-ONE

Though both were unemployed, Brantley and Christy now had a job to do.

It was something they couldn't do alone. They had to enlist the help of several people, some of whom would be only too eager to help, some who would need convincing.

Christy had needed convincing at the start. But Brantley had worked on her with his old charm and self-assurance.

'We could pull that off?' she had asked.

'Sure,' Brantley had said. 'If some kid from the mailroom suddenly moved into an executive position, would you tell him he could never pull it off?'

'But you didn't.'

Brantley cleared his throat. 'Almost did. And we can pull this off, too — almost . . . maybe . . . '

Melrose was the next to bring aboard. Brantley did not think it would be difficult. He was right.

'Is it something I could get fired for?' Melrose had asked.

'You might,' Brantley said.

'Okay,' he answered. 'Live dangerously. What the hell.'

There was still one person they had to convince. Brantley was nervous but hopeful: Vera Prescott was usually open to suggestions.

The day of their attack was an important day for Pemrose. It was the day Donald Davenport was meeting with Howard Prescott and company.

The meeting took place in the Pemrose conference room. There was no informality this time; each executive sat straight up, fear on his face, hope in his heart. Maybe it wouldn't be so bad, each thought.

But Donald Davenport was even worse than any of them had expected. A man twice the size of Howard Prescott, he radiated not so much power as blind appetite. He dwarfed Prescott just as Prescott dwarfed his employees. Though there was some pleasure in seeing the boss brought down to size, each executive felt himself shrinking, too; there was no pleasure in that.

Each team had brought lawyers, accountants and supporters. Davenport and Prescott sat at opposite ends of the big table. Each maintained an air of cordiality, but there was no mistaking the fact that Prescott was being swallowed. And Davenport's smile said he gave his compliments to the chef.

'Of course, Mr Davenport,' Prescott said, 'we realize that you will want to be moving some of your own people into medium-control positions at Pemrose.'

'Naturally,' Davenport said.

'What we are concerned about, quite frankly, is the upper-management positions.'

'Most of them will have to go.'

Prescott took a deep breath. He could feel his team growing more shaky beside him. 'I see.'

'But a handful of them — who have been so helpful, like yourselves, of course — will be staying on as long as you like.'

This cheered Prescott. He looked over at Art Thomas and the others, as if to say, See what I did for you? All of them smiled back, enormously relieved.

'Then I see nothing,' Davenport said, 'to stand in the way of an immediate merger of our two compan —'

Something stood in the way then. Brantley stood in the doorway.

He looked around with an innocent air. He had on his

good blue suit, yet he was even less than a mailroom clerk today.

'Is this the place?' he blurted out. 'Oh, good. Sorry we're late.'

He walked further in, undaunted. Behind him followed in succession Christy, Melrose and Jean.

Davenport was confused. He tried to laugh off this interruption; he turned to Prescott for some explanation. Prescott was clearly enraged. He talked through his teeth to Thomas.

'Get them out of here . . .'

Thomas rose, obediently. He ran to stop Brantley and his party from advancing one step farther.

'This is an important private meeting,' he said. 'You can't come in here. All of you will have to leave.'

Melrose gave Thomas a polite smile. Then he reached out and took the dutiful executive's hand.

'Hold this, will you?' he said.

Melrose took the gum from his mouth, pressed it into Thomas' hand, and closed his fingers over it.

'Thanks.'

The former mailroom employee then sat down at the table, along with Brantley and Christy and Jean. All were making themselves comfortable when Prescott gave another executive an order.

'Call Building Security,' he said.

The aide moved quickly to a telephone. But Brantley only stared down Prescott.

'Relax, Howard,' he said, cavalierly. 'Speaking for the personnel in the mailroom and the secretarial pool, we're here to give our blessings to this merger.'

Davenport obviously found this very unorthodox, not to mention distasteful. He looked over at Prescott.

'Who in the hell are these people?'

Brantley gave a great grin at Davenport now.

'Don — glad you could come. Anybody mind if I stand up? I always think better when I'm moving around.'

Finding no objections — all were too stunned to reply — Brantley stood and began to pace.

'I've gotta tell you,' he said, 'I didn't like the idea of a merger at first. Bad idea. But I was wrong. The more I thought about it, the more I realized that our products and your distribution capabilities could vault Pemrose right to the top of the market.'

Davenport spoke up, harshly. 'So glad you approve, whoever you are. Now, if you'll get the hell out of here, we'll finish the job.'

Brantley shrugged, good-naturedly, 'Can't do that. You see, the big problem here is management. I mean, it was bad enough before, having this place run by Prescott, but now the company has a guy like *you* to deal with, too.'

Christy joined him then. Brantley took a polite step back, so attention would not be diverted from her.

'You sell off the crown jewels and leave a shell,' she said. 'You're a true raider — you take your profit, then run the company into the ground. That sort of ruins the potential of the merger, doesn't it?'

Davenport did not care to dignify the question. He shot off an order to Prescott. 'Get them out of here. Now.'

Christy laughed. 'He can't, Mr Davenport.'

'Call him Don,' Brantley instructed.

'He can't get us out of here, Don. You see, Brantley made arrangements to buy five percent of the stock in your company, Davenport Enterprises, this morning. We just filed a 13-D.'

Davenport's eyes bulged. '*What*?'

'That's correct,' Brantley said. 'We're here to inform you of our intent to initiate a takeover of Davenport Enterprises and a proxy fight for the Pemrose Corporation.'

The room suddenly exploded with confusion. All looked with amazement, derision and fear at the intruders. Then they had three *more* people to contend with.

Melrose had risen and moved to the door. Through it, he let in three men. One was serene, one was fat and funny, one was magnetic.

Owens, Fletcher and McMartin were joining *this* party now.

'These are my financial advisors,' Brantley said. 'They agreed to lend me the money to finance this takeover.'

Prescott stared at the men Vera had pointed out to Brantley during the party. Men with whom Prescott had gone swimming, played tennis, gotten drunk.

'Gentlemen,' he said, 'surely you're not willing to invest in some cockeyed scheme dreamed up by a kid who worked in our mailroom!'

Brantley was the one who replied. 'Not at first they weren't. But I had an ace in the hole — a major stock-holder in the company who had the clout and support I needed. Don, I'd like you to meet the chairperson of the Pemrose Foundation.'

Brantley extended his hand towards the open door. Entering sleekly through it, making the kind of grand entrance she had always dreamed about, was Vera Prescott.

She walked over with the greatest style; she had never looked more elegant. Prescott had never looked more displeased.

'Brantley and I are very old friends,' she announced, 'and when he told me all his wonderful ideas for running the company, I knew he was the man for the job.'

Prescott looked with disgust upon the woman who shared his name. He thought now would be the perfect time — and maybe his last chance — to air some dirty linen.

'I think we all understand your *real* motivation here, Vera,' he said.

Vera only shrugged. 'I admit that I felt some attraction

185

toward Brantley at the start. But love is love and business is business. You've run this company into the ground, Howard, and I believe these people here can bring it back to where it belongs again.'

Vera had reached Prescott. She tugged on his arm — not with affection, with insistence.

'Now up, Howard, out of that chair. Brantley, you take Howard's place.'

Prescott was fuming — and not budging. 'Don't be ridiculous! I'm not resigning my position.'

'You don't have to, Howard,' she said. 'You're fired.'

'What?! You can't —'

'Oh, yes, I can. I've contacted several of our major stockholders and as of this afternoon I control fifty point one percent of the voting stock. You, too, Art —' she pointed at Thomas, 'you're gone. Over here, Brantley. You, too, Christy. Melrose, Jean, over here.'

The new Pemrose team began to rise to take their new positions. As they were moving, two security guards appeared at the door.

Vera was glad to see them.

'Just in time, gentlemen,' she said. 'Mr Prescott and his aides have disrupted a very important meeting here. Would you please escort them out of the building?'

The security guards moved round the table. Prescott and his friends all rose, with the deepest reluctance. He shot one more murderous look at his wife. Then, proudly, he led the parade out of the room. He would be head of something, even if it were only head of the has-beens.

There was a pause after they were all gone. Then Vera smiled sweetly at Brantley and took her seat.

'Would you take charge of the meeting now, Brantley?'

Brantley nodded his thanks. Then he turned to Davenport. The millionaire only stared cruelly at the boy with the mediocre suit who was now in command.

186

'Don,' Brantley began, 'we're all men of the world here and this is how it's going to be. You have thirty days to have your attorneys prepare all papers of transference, delivering your company and all its holdings into the hands of Pemrose Corporation.'

CHAPTER THIRTY-TWO

Brantley's penthouse had a wonderful view.

He could see all of Manhattan from it; he could even see the top of the Pemrose building. Adjusting the tie on his tuxedo, he sipped from his champagne. Then he winked hello at some more arriving guests.

The place was ideal for his purposes: the sunken living room, the spacious den, the two bedrooms and the terrace afforded plenty of space. It gave waiters plenty of room to serve caviar; to give traveling violinists lots of elbow room.

The man to whom he was talking now was giving him a headache. He didn't want to discuss business tonight; this was going to be a night on the town.

'Knock it off, will you?' Brantley said. 'Ever since I made you a vice-president, you've been acting like a suit.'

Melrose took affront. He adjusted his cummerbund. 'You don't have to be insulting.'

Vera slunk over to them now. She was at her most alluring in a low-cut gown. She slipped her arm into Melrose's.

'Let's go, Freddy,' she said. 'We'll be late for the opera.'

'Yes, dear.' Melrose turned to Brantley. 'See you later, pal.'

Brantley waved goodbye to the two of them. Such a cute couple, he thought.

He looked around to make sure he was not being watched. Then he dug into his pocket and took out a

189

jewelry case. He examined the contents one final time and smiled, approvingly. Then he went to find the recipient of this gift.

He found her standing at the picture window, staring at the view. Her back was bare; her shoulders seemed to shine.

Brantley sneaked up behind Christy, He kissed one shoulder and then the other. She turned, surprised.

'Happy first anniversary, darling,' he said.

He handed over the jewelry case. She looked at him, as if to say, You shouldn't have. Then she opened it.

Lying on the velvet inside were a new ballpoint pen and a sweetheart rose.

'Brantley,' she said, 'you're too extravagant. It's lovely.'

Brantley laughed. Then he reached into another pocket and pulled out a diamond bracelet. He let it dangle on the end of his fingers.

'Almost forgot,' he said. 'This came with it.'

Christy laughed and kissed him. They held each other for a minute, shaking their heads against each other, as if still amazed at their good fortune.

Their celebration was short-lived. Brantley's chauffeur had arrived, holding both of their coats.

'Your car is ready, sir,' Barney Brady said.

'Brady —' Brantley said, 'how many times do I have to tell you?'

'Sorry. Your car is ready, Mr College Puke, sir.'

Brantley smiled. 'More like it. Are you ready, Christy?'

'Ready, darling.'

'After you drop us off at the theater, take the rest of the night off, Brady,' he said. 'We'll ride home with the Melroses.'

Brady was pleased. 'Thank you, Mr College Puke, sir!'

Brantley and Christy made their way carefully through the enormous apartment, as if still negotiating their way into the world of the rich. Brantley knew its worth was only relative. It would have meant little if he was still Carlton Whitfield, still more and less than himself. He thought even his parents would be proud — if they ever got the courage to come to New York.

As for Christy, there was no placing a figure on how much *she* was worth. Brantley Foster may have been Brantley Foster, but he couldn't have done it alone. She had been his ace in the hole; love had been the secret of his success.

He turned off the lights. Then they went out together into the New York night.

THE END

A SELECTED LIST OF
FILM & TV TIE-INS FROM CORGI BOOKS

THE PRICES SHOWN BELOW WERE CORRECT AT THE TIME OF GOING TO PRESS.
HOWEVER TRANSWORLD PUBLISHERS RESERVE THE RIGHT TO SHOW NEW
RETAIL PRICES ON COVERS WHICH MAY DIFFER FROM THOSE PREVIOUSLY
ADVERTISED IN THE TEXT OR ELSEWHERE.

☐	12160 6	**MANHUNTER**	Thomas Harris	£2.50
☐	13263 2	**THE THREE AMIGOS**	Leonore Fleischer	£2.50
☐	12795 7	**BROND**	Frederic Lindsay	£2.50
☐	13132 6	**SNOW ON THE WIND**	Hugh Miller	£1.95
☐	13133 4	**DISTRICT NURSE**	Hugh Miller	£2.50
☐	17241 7	**DEADLY FRIEND**	Diana Henstell	£2.50
☐	13148 2	**APRIL FOOL'S DAY**	Jeff Rovin	£1.95
☐	13135 0	**POLTERGEIST II**	James Kahn	£1.95
☐	12881 3	**TARGET**	Stephen Hunter	£1.95
☐	12802 3	**ENEMY MINE** David Gerrold & Barry B. Longyear		£1.95
☐	12774 4	**BACK TO THE FUTURE**	George Gipe	£1.95
☐	12522 9	**GREMLINS**	George Gipe	£1.95
☐	52263 5	**GREMLINS (Children's Edition)**	George Gipe	£1.25
☐	12634 9	**ROMANCING THE STONE**	Joan Wilder	£1.75
☐	12363 3	**THE BOUNTY**	Richard Hough	£1.95
☐	99209 7	**THE HOTEL NEW HAMPSHIRE**	John Irving	£4.95
☐	17388 X	**FERRIS BUELLER'S DAY OFF**	Todd Strasser	£1.95
☐	11610 6	**SOPHIE'S CHOICE**	William Styron	£2.50
☐	11750 1	**RAIDERS OF THE LOST ARK**	Campbell Black	£1.50

*All these books are available at your book shop or newsagent, or can be ordered direct from the publisher.
Just tick the titles you want and fill in the form below.*

Transworld Publishers, Cash Sales Department, 61-63 Uxbridge Road, Ealing, London, W5 5SA.

Please send a cheque or postal order, not cash. All cheques and postal orders must be in £ sterling
and made payable to Transworld Publishers Ltd.
Please allow cost of book(s) plus the following for postage and packing:

UK/Republic of Ireland Customers:
Orders in excess of £5; no charge. Orders under £5; add 50p.

Overseas Customers:
All orders; add £1.50.

NAME (Block Letters): ....

ADDRESS ....

....